Information and Communication Technology

KEY STAGE 2: YEAR 4 PRIMARY 5

Frances Mackay

Contents

Introduction

 ABOUT THE SERIES 

Developing ICT Skills is a series of books written specifically to complement the QCA and DfEE *Information Technology Scheme of Work for Key Stages 1 and 2*. There is one book for each year from Reception/Year 1 (Scottish Primary 1/2), through Key Stage 1 to Year 6 (Scottish Primary 7) at the end of Key Stage 2.

The series offers a structured approach with the non-specialist in mind and provides detailed lesson plans to teach specific ICT skills. A unique feature of the series is the provision of differentiated photocopiable activities designed to support each lesson. Most of these activities are independent tasks that can be completed away from the computer or IT equipment being used, thereby enabling the teacher to work with a focus group at the computer. The differentiation of the activities considerably reduces teacher preparation time when planning group work.

The lessons have been specifically written for the classroom with access to only one computer but will, of course, work equally well in a computer suite situation.

Accompanying each of the two books for Key Stage 1 is a CD-Rom, produced by AirCom International, that contains activities designed to support each lesson. Schools will not, therefore, need a separate word-processor, art or music package, for example, to teach the ICT skills being addressed. If schools prefer to use their own computer programs, however, the books are designed to stand alone without the accompanying CD-Rom.

 ABOUT THIS BOOK 

This book is for teachers of Year 4 (Scottish Primary level 5) children. It aims to:

- ✦ develop children's ICT skills through a series of structured lessons aimed at increasing children's awareness of the strengths and limitations of ICT;
- ✦ support teachers by providing practical teaching methods and activity ideas based on whole-class, group, paired and individual teaching;
- ✦ support non-specialist teachers by providing structured lesson plans with practical ideas and 'specialist tips' designed to address some of the common problems the children (and teachers!) may experience;
- ✦ provide lessons that are cross-curricular wherever possible;
- ✦ encourage the children to recognise the importance of ICT in everyday experiences;
- ✦ encourage enjoyment as well as confidence in using ICT skills.

✦ LESSON CONTENT 

 Learning objectives

This sets out the specific learning objectives for each lesson.

 Resources

This is a list of what you will need to do the lessons.

 Whole class introduction

This provides ideas for introducing the activity, and may include key questions to ask the children, so that they can move on to their group task having learned concepts and the vocabulary they will need for the group activities.

 Group activities

Focus group – with the teacher

This follows the whole class introduction and is a teaching session with the teacher working together with the children at the computer (or other ICT equipment). The teaching in this session can either be carried out with the class as a whole (by using a computer and a projected screen or by using a computer suite) or within a small group while the rest of the class do the photocopiable activity sheets (if appropriate) or another (sometimes related) independent task. This section contains suggestions for teaching the key concepts and skills relating directly to the ICT learning objectives for the lesson. Hints and tips are provided to help support the teacher when introducing these skills.

Using the activity sheets

The activity sheets provide three activities that can be done more or less independently from the teacher. These sheets are differentiated so that the same task can be completed by below average, average and above average children at their own level. Activity sheet 1 tasks are the easiest and Activity sheet 3 the hardest. In most cases, the sheets contain tasks that are designed to be completed away from the computer or ICT equipment being used but reinforce the skills that will be used at the computer itself. Many activities are also designed so the children can compare a manual task with a computer one (editing text, for example), thereby enabling a discussion during the plenary session about the strengths and limitations of ICT.

Introduction

Sometimes, the sheets can be completed immediately after the whole class introduction (so some children may be working with the teacher in a small group at the computer while the rest are completing the sheets). At other times, the sheets are to be completed only after the children have experienced the focus group session. (In a classroom with only one computer then, the children may need to be set other independent tasks until they have been part of the focus group.)

For each lesson then, each child should experience the whole class introduction and a focus group session as well as completing an activity sheet. In classrooms with only one computer this means the teacher may need to organise the lesson over a week, for example:

Mon	whole class introduction group A – with the teacher at computer (focus group session) groups B, C and D – completing activity sheets
Tues	group B – focus group session group A – activity sheet groups C and D – independent tasks
Wed	group C – focus group session groups A, B and D – independent tasks
Thurs	group D – focus group session groups A, B and C – independent tasks plenary – all groups

✦ *Plenary session*

This suggests ideas for a whole-class review to discuss the learning outcomes, and gives questions to ask so that the children have a chance to reflect on what they have learned and for the teacher to assess their knowledge and understanding. This session may not necessarily take place on the same day as the whole class introduction – it may come at the end of the week after all the children have completed their focus group session and activity sheets.

APPENDIX

At the back of this book are some extra photocopiable pages. Page 62 offers suggestions for how these pages could be used. Most of the pages have been prepared for the teacher to use as resources for particular lessons but there are also ideas on how to use the pages to develop further activities in follow-up sessions. Where relevant, these pages also contain the answers to particular activity sheets.

Page 76 is an assessment sheet that outlines the basic concepts and skills that a Year 4 child should experience. The teacher can photocopy this page for each child and, together with the work produced from each lesson, use it to compile a comprehensive individual ICT profile to make assessments and determine future targets.

HARDWARE REQUIREMENTS

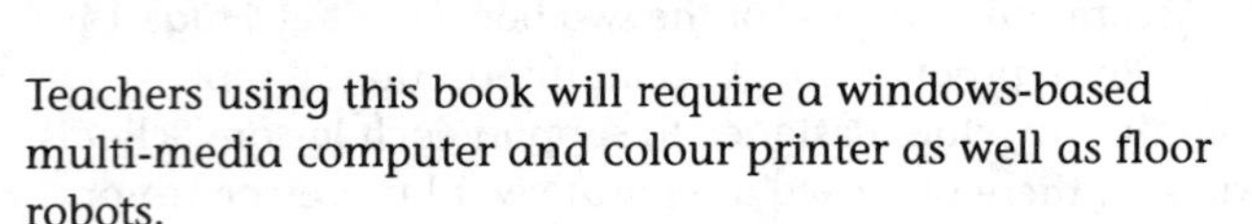

Teachers using this book will require a windows-based multi-media computer and colour printer as well as floor robots.

SOFTWARE REQUIREMENTS

The following software is needed:

- a WYSIWYG (What You See Is What You Get) word-processor;
- a paint program with a symmetry tool;
- a branching database program;
- a data handling package;
- a version of LOGO (or any other similar program) that includes the commands 'clear', 'penup' and 'pendown' and which allows the final results to be printed out.

Introduction

TEACHING ICT

For many of today's adults there has always been a degree of mystique surrounding ICT skills. Some people have even avoided contact with computers altogether! However, in the teaching profession, this is not an option. In truth, there is nothing difficult about acquiring or teaching ICT skills, and in fact, there has never been a better or more exciting time to become a computer user. To become a confident ICT user, teacher or pupil, you need to be taught a few basic skills and you need the opportunity to become familiar with the way the technology works, but you do not need to become an expert. The National Curriculum requires ICT to be taught to all pupils and this can seem daunting if the teacher is learning alongside the pupils. In this series we aim to provide the teacher with the materials, skills and knowledge that will make covering the ICT Scheme of Work an achievable and positive experience. We expect children who take part in the lessons to learn age-appropriate ICT skills and to become discerning users of technology.

Schools that teach ICT skills discretely then transfer those skills to other subject areas find that children achieve higher levels of ICT competence than when ICT skills are **only** taught through other subjects. This suggests that teachers should set aside time specifically for the teaching of ICT skills. This does not mean that it is necessary to timetable ICT lessons every week but it is important to make sure some ICT lessons are devoted to the teaching of specific ICT skills. This can be carried out through occasional whole class lessons as well as small group or individual lessons and does not necessarily require the whole class to be working on ICT at the same time. The lessons in this book agree with this premise and ICT is the main focus of each one. However, where there are opportunities for links with other curriculum areas, these have been made.

Prior to the publication of the QCA and DfEE IT SoW it was difficult for schools to know exactly what ICT skills should be taught to each year group. We have now been presented with a clear and comprehensive guide which clearly demonstrates continuity and progression. If the teacher is working with older children who have not had the opportunity to acquire the rudimentary skills, it would be best to work at the correct level for these children. Hence the years and levels suggested in the IT SoW and in this series of books are to be taken as desirable guidelines.

In order to achieve a high level of success for the children, teaching intentions should be very clear and built within a whole-school scheme of work that demonstrates evident continuity and progression of concepts and skills. This is extremely important in ICT because today, perhaps more than ever before, children vary considerably in their ICT capabilities. Many children who have access to ICT outside school can appear to have greater skills in handling software and hardware but teachers need to be aware that these children may not necessarily have the full range of ICT capabilites expected of them in the programmes of study. Regular observations and assessments are therefore necessary to ascertain the best tasks and experiences to support the children's learning.

Reliability of the technology has often been one of the biggest hurdles for schools! Therefore, before the teacher begins to use the lessons in this series, we recommend that he or she checks that all the necessary equipment is working correctly. Access to broken or out-of-date technology is time wasting and very frustrating for teachers and children alike.

Published by Hopscotch Educational Publishing Company Ltd,
29 Waterloo Place, Leamington Spa CV32 5LA 01926 744227

Written by Frances Mackay
Series consultant – Ayleen Driver
Series design by Blade Communications
Illustrated by The Drawing Room
Cover illustration by Susan Hutchison
Printed by Clintplan, Southam

ISBN 1-902239-43-1

Lesson 1

Using fonts

Learning objectives

- To explore the use of presentation techniques in newspapers.
- To compose newspaper headlines.
- To alter the font size and use effects to indicate relative importance of text using a word-processor.

Resources

- Photocopiable page 63.
- Newspapers.
- A word-processing program.

Whole class introduction

- Provide each pair of children with a newspaper. Ask them to flip through it and, without reading the articles, list things they notice about how print is used on the pages.
- Share their responses. Discuss the meaning of the terms 'headline', 'sub-heading', 'caption' and 'paragraph' and ask them to tell you what they notice about the size of the print for each of these features. Why do they think the headings and sub-headings are different-sized print? Are some words in bold? Why? Are some words underlined? Why? Which part of a page are they attracted to? Why do they think this is? Does the changing text size in an article draw the reader into it?
- Look at examples of headlines. What do they notice about them? Are they in sentences? Do they use words and phrases that grab attention? Do front-page headlines help to sell the paper? How difficult might it be to write them?
- Share photocopiable page 63 so that the children can explore these questions further. Read out the article with the children following the text. Why do they think the first paragraph is in bolder print? Explain that the article does not have a headline and that their task is to choose one. In pairs, ask them to select the most appropriate words and size for the headline and tell them that they must be prepared to give their reasons why.
- Share their ideas. Which headline do they think would attract the most attention? Why? Which one do they think is least effective? Why? What size of print is best? Why?

Group activities

Focus group – with the teacher

- Remind the children about how a newspaper uses different text sizes and effects to indicate the importance of different headlines. Explain that people use computers to write articles in the newspaper and therefore they need to know how to change the appearance and size of the text. Tell them that you will be showing them how this is done on the word-processor.
- Demonstrate how to change the font size and use bold and underline. Show them how to return the words to the way they were. Show them how to select pieces of text. (Usually by positioning the mouse so that the screen arrow is at the start of the text, clicking the left mouse button and holding it down whilst dragging over the text. To select all the text, go to edit and click on 'select all'.)
- Now ask them to make up one front page headline, two other headlines, a sub-heading and a caption. Ask them to select the most suitable font size (and bold and underline if appropriate) to indicate their order of importance and type the list in order of priority. Ask them to print them out when they are satisfied with the results.

Using the photocopiable activity sheets

- Use the activity sheets to reinforce the lesson.

Plenary session

Share the responses to the activity sheets, asking the children to give reasons why they selected particular headlines. Share the computer lists. Have they used size/bold to indicate importance? What problems did they have? How did they resolve them?

Name ____________________ **Activity 1** Date ____________________

✦ Newspaper headlines ✦

✦ The three headlines below all belong on this page from a newspaper. Decide which one you think should be the main headline, which would be a sub-heading for that story and which is the heading for the other story. Write them on the page in the size you think they should be.

Shepton gets £10 000 award!

Clean-up to start soon

Local woman wins prize

It was announced today that the hard-working Shepton Residents' Group will be awarded an amazing £10 000 to begin their clean-up campaign in the town of Shepton.

Mr Miles, a spokesperson for the group, said he was absolutely delighted that Shepton will finally be able to get rid of all the rubbish that is littered all over the town's parks and footpaths. He said that the award money will be used to repair broken park benches, buy new litter bins and plant trees and flowers.

The award money was presented to Mr Miles today at a special lunch held at Shepton Hotel. Everyone at the lunch was thrilled that their town could at last become a better place in which to live.

Mrs Dorothy Green of James Square was very pleased to learn today that her paintings of Gilby have won a national art prize in the Bell Exhibition.

Mrs Green's watercolours can be seen on display at Gilby Town Hall from 2-5pm every day this week.

✦ Now draw a picture to go with the main story.

On the back of this page, invent two main headlines of your own.

Name ____________ **Activity 2** Date ____________

✦ Newspaper headlines ✦

✦ Below are some headlines and sub-headings from a newspaper. Write a heading and sub-heading of your own.

New solar-powered car wows car fans

School wins environment award

Is your car now out of date?

Award buys new playground

✦ Decide which headline should be the main one for the front page below. Write it out in the style and size you think it should be. Then write its sub-heading underneath. Now write the story to go with the heading. Draw a picture in the box.

Name ______________________ **Activity 3** Date ______________________

✦ Newspaper headlines ✦

✦ Invent four headlines and four matching sub-headings for the front page of a newspaper. Write them here.

✦ Decide which headline should be the main one for the front page below. Set out the page with the headline and sub-heading in the style and size you think they should be. Write the story to go with the headline.

Lesson 2

Reordering text

Learning objectives

- To understand that information that is ordered sequentially provides better coherence and meaning.
- To know that ICT can be used to reorganise text.
- To use 'cut' and 'paste' facilities in a word-processor to reorder text.

Resources

- Photocopiable page 64.
- Blu-Tack
- A word processing program.

Whole class introduction

- Enlarge page 64. Explain to the children that they are going to learn how to set out instructions. Show them photocopiable page 64 and explain that it is a set of instructions on how to grow some potatoes. Share the text. What problem is there in understanding the instructions? How could we improve them?
- Point out the three sub-headings at the top of the page. Would these help us to order the instructions more clearly? Using a different coloured pen for each sub-heading, agree which pieces of text belong to each one and underline or tick them.
- Cut out the pieces of text and use Blu-Tack to 'paste' them under the correct sub-headings. What else needs to be done? Discuss how important it is to have some parts of the instructions in the correct order. Compare this with using a recipe. How important is it to follow the recipe in order? What might happen if you did not?
- Discuss how the correct order could be shown – by numbering, for example. Is it important for the text under the sub-heading 'What you need' to be in a certain order? What about 'What to do' and 'Things to know'?
- Agree the ordering of the text in the 'What to do' section and rearrange the text.
- Reread the text – is it more coherent now? Is the meaning of the text now clear? Explain that they will be carrying out a similar task themselves, using an activity sheet and the computer.

Group activities

Focus group – with the teacher

- Before the lesson, enter on the computer a set of instructions in the incorrect order. Explain to the children that you are going to show them how to 'cut' and 'paste' on the computer in the same way as they did using the activity sheets. Remind them how to select text (refer to page 6). Show them how to use the 'cut' and 'paste' facilities on the word-processor to move text around the screen.
- Now ask them to use 'cut' and 'paste' to reorder the sentences in the set of instructions.
- Ask them to print out their work. (Don't save the work so the text remains the same each time a new group works at the computer.)
  Note: it may be wise to keep another copy of the file by choosing 'save as' from the 'file' menu. Give it a different name.

Using the photocopiable activity sheets

- Use the sheets before the computer session.

Plenary session

Share the responses to the activity sheets. Does everyone agree on the order of the instructions? Is it possible to have a different order and still make sense? Compare the physical cut and paste using the activity sheets with the screen cutting and pasting – which is easier/ more convenient? Which one ends up with a better final presentation? What uses can the children suggest for using the 'cut' and 'paste' facilities on the computer? How will it help them when using the word-processor?

Name ______________________ **Activity 1** Date ______________________

✦ A plant waterer ✦

✦ Below are some instructions to make a plant waterer. The instructions in the last part of the 'What to do' section are in the wrong order. Cut them out and put them in the correct order. Number them. Then cut out the top part of the instructions and glue all the pieces onto another sheet of paper. Write a heading and do a border.

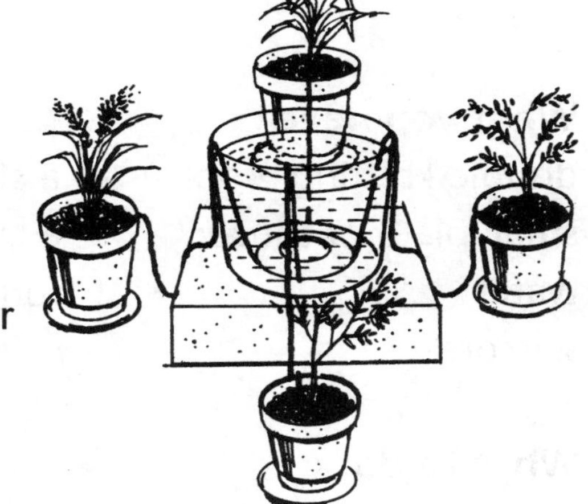

What you need:

double knitting wool
small plate or saucer
water
scissors
a strong box
a large water container
four pot plants

What to do:

1 Fill the container with water.
2 Place the container on the box.
3 Arrange the pot plants in a circle around the container.

Gather together all the ends of the wool in the container and place the small plate over them to ensure that the wool is always at the bottom of the container.

Cut the wool into four 1 metre lengths.

Make sure the other end of each strand of wool is in the container.

Place one end of each strand of wool into the top of each plant pot.

Put the cut lengths of wool into the water until they are well soaked.

Name ____________________ **Activity 2** Date ____________________

✦ A plant waterer ✦

✦ Below are some instructions to make a plant waterer. The instructions in the 'What to do' section are all mixed up. Cut out each part and put them in the correct order. Number them. Cut out the 'What you need' section and then glue all the pieces onto another sheet of paper. Write a heading and do a border.

What you need:

double knitting wool
small plate or saucer
water
scissors
a strong box
a large water container
four pot plants

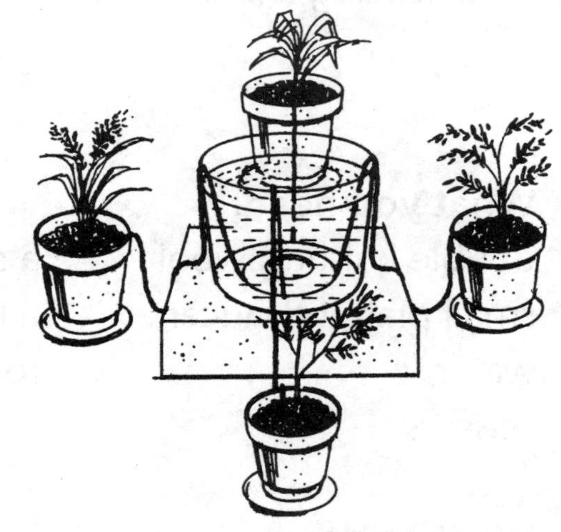

What to do:

Arrange the pot plants in a circle around the container.

Gather together all the ends of the wool in the container and place the small plate over them to ensure that the wool is always at the bottom of the container.

Fill the container with water.

Put the cut lengths of wool into the water until they are well soaked.

Place the container on the box.

Place one end of each strand of wool into the top of each pot plant.

Cut the wool into four 1 metre lengths.

Make sure the other end of each strand of wool is in the container.

Name ____________________ **Activity 3** Date ____________________

✦ A plant waterer ✦

✦ Below are some instructions for making a plant waterer. However, the instructions are all mixed up. Cut out each part and put them under the correct heading in the correct order. Glue onto another piece of paper. Write a heading and do a border.

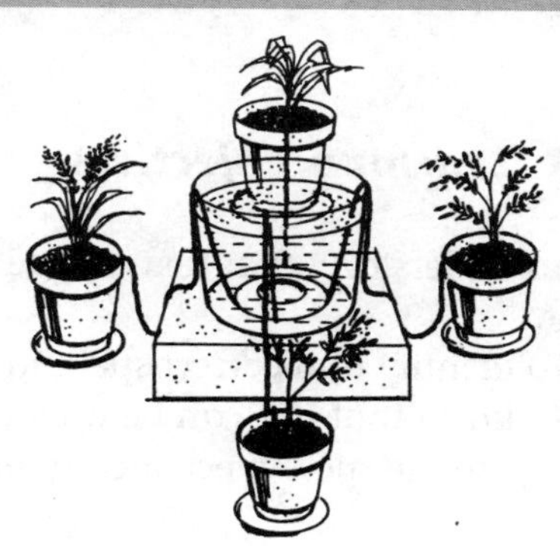

What you need:

What to do:

How it works:

Fill the container with water.

double knitting wool

Cut the wool into four 1 metre lengths.

Place one end of each strand of wool into the top of each pot plant.

water

Place the container on the box.

scissors

Put the cut lengths of wool into the water until they are well soaked.

The water from the container is passed to the plants by capillary action of the wool fibres.

Gather together all the ends of the wool in the container and place the small plate over them to ensure that the wool is always at the bottom of the container.

small plate or saucer

a strong box

Arrange the pot plants in a circle around the container.

Make sure the other end of each strand of wool is in the container.

four pot plants

a large water container

Lesson 3

Editing text – 1

Learning objectives

- ✦ To understand that text can be edited to improve it.
- ✦ To identify and correct spelling errors in a text.
- ✦ To know that ICT can be used to correct mistakes.
- ✦ To use the spell-check facility in a word-processor.

Resources

- ✦ Photocopiable page 65.
- ✦ Dictionaries
- ✦ A word-processing program.

Whole class introduction

- ✦ Enlarge all or part of page 65. Explain to the children that they are going to learn some proof-reading skills. Discuss 'proof-reading' and give examples of when it might be used. Tell them that before books, newspapers and magazines are published, editors and proof-readers check the writing to correct any mistakes and to make sure the sentences make sense. Why is this important?
- ✦ Explain that today they will be concentrating on checking a text for spelling mistakes. Share page 65. Read it out, making sure the children can see the words. Ask them to tell you the mistakes they noticed. Correct the errors by crossing out the original word and writing in the correct one. How can we check to see that we are right? Remind them about the importance of using dictionaries. If appropriate, revise how dictionaries work by looking up words such as 'nitrous', 'methane' or 'chlorofluorocarbon'.
- ✦ Discuss how spelling errors can also be ones of context, for example the use of 'than' instead of 'then' or words that sound the same but have a different meaning, such as 'plaice' instead of 'place' and 'son' instead of 'sun'. How many of these examples can they find in the text?
- ✦ Tell the children that they will be carrying out a similar task using an activity sheet and that you will also be showing them how spelling can be corrected using a spell-checker in a word-processing program.

Group activities

Focus group – with the teacher

- ✦ Before the lesson, enter on the computer an extract similar to that on page 65, with spelling mistakes in it. Show the children the corrected version of page 65. Ask them to tell you what the page now looks like. Does it look untidy? Is it difficult to read? What would they need to do to produce a 'good' copy? Explain that if they use a word-processor, they can correct their mistakes on screen, thereby keeping the page tidy and then print out the 'good' copy as a final version.
- ✦ Demonstrate the spell-checker. Show how it sometimes provides a number of suggestions for each word, such as 'wry', 'word' and 'wad' for 'wrd'. Why would it do this? Explain that the first suggestion is not always the right one and the correct word may not even be listed! Remind them about the mistakes on page 65 where the spelling was correct but the context was not, such as 'than' for 'then'. Explain why the spell-checker will not pick up these errors and that it is important for the children to check the text themselves.
- ✦ Ask them to use the spell-checker and their own knowledge to correct the mistakes in the text (you may need to remind them how to delete and replace text) and to print it out. Ask them not to save their work as they go, or at the end, so that the same text can be reloaded and used again.

Using the photocopiable activity sheets

- ✦ Use the sheets before the computer session.

Plenary session

Share the responses to the activity sheets. Did everyone find all the mistakes? Did they use dictionaries to help them? Compare the activities on the sheets with the computer one. What advantages and disadvantages are there in using a computer spell-checker? Discuss how hand-held computer checkers can also be used to check their writing.

Name ____________________ **Activity 1** Date ____________________

✦ Acid rain ✦

✦ The underlined words in the sentences below are all spelled incorrectly. Use a dictionary to find the correct spellings. Write the correct spellings above each word. You should also find two other mistakes. Circle and correct them.

Rain <u>warter</u> usually has <u>sum</u> acid in it but it is <u>becomeing</u> worse.

The acid gets into the air from <u>factry</u> pollution, coal and oil-fired power stations and car <u>exhoust</u> fumes.

Acid rain can <u>caus</u> fish to die in rivers and <u>lackes</u>.

Acid rain causes <u>meny</u> trees and plants to die.

Acid rain can harme people's <u>healthe</u>.

In Whales, the numbers of dippers have fallen <u>becorse</u> the <u>insecks</u> that this bird eats have been killed by acid rain.

Name ____________________ **Activity 2** **Date** ____________________

✦ Acid rain ✦

✦ Read through the following information. In each paragraph you will find three spelling mistakes. Underline the mistakes and write the correct spellings above each word. Use a dictionary to help you.

Rain warter usualy has sum acid in it but over the past few decades it has become worse.

The acid gets into the air from factry pollution and the fumes from coal and oil-fired power stations. The xhaust fumes from cars and lorrys can also turn into acid in the air.

When it raines, the acid then eats away at the stone and iron on biuldings and it polutes rivers, lakes and the soil.

Acid rain causes plants and trees to die. Meny forests in Europe are dyeing and this meens that the animals who live in the forests are also suffering.

Lots of lakes in Europe and Amerika have bean affected by acid rain. It kills the fishe that live there.

In Whales, the numbers of dippers have fallen becorse the insecks this bird eats have been killed by acid rain.

We need to stop air polution in all countrys of the world if we are to stop the damege caused by acid rain.

Name ____________________ **Activity 3** **Date** ____________________

✦ Acid rain ✦

✦ Read through the following information and correct all the spelling mistakes. You should find 21 different mistakes. Use a dictionary to help you.

Rainwarter is normally slightley acidic but over the past few decades it has become much worse. This is becase of air polution. Coal and oil-fired power stations produse sulphur dioxide that can tern into deadly sulphuric acid. The xhaust fumes from cars and lorries produce nitrogen oxide that can turn into nitric acid. When it rains, the acid than eats away at the stone and iron work on buildings and pollutes rivers, lakes and soil.

Trees get there nutrients from the soil. In areas where there are large amounts of acid in the soil, these nutrients are washed away and the trees starve to death. Over halve of West Germany's great forests are thort to be dead or dyeing because of acid rain. Other countries in Europe are allso suffering. When trees and plants die in an area this meens that the animals that live on and around them also suffer.

Thousands of European and Amerikan lakes have been poisioned by acid rain, killing most of the fish that lived there. In Whales, the numbers of dippers have drasticaly fallen because the freshwater insects that this bird eats have bean killed by acid rain.

We need to reduce air pollution in all countrys of the world if we are to stop the terrable damage caused by acid rain.

Editing text – 2

Learning objectives

- ✦ To revise how pronouns are used to distinguish gender.
- ✦ To change the gender of pronouns in a text.
- ✦ To know that ICT can be used to automate the amendment of text.
- ✦ To amend text using 'find and replace' in a word-processor.

Resources

- ✦ Photocopiable page 66.
- ✦ A word-processing program.

Whole class introduction

- ✦ Enlarge page 66. Remind the children about the editing work they carried out in Lesson 3. Tell them that they are to carry out some more editing tasks – this time looking at the use of pronouns. Revise what pronouns are, especially those in the third person.
- ✦ Share page 66, making sure all the children can see the text. Tell them that the text was written for a school magazine. Why do they think the author wanted to write about Alex? Ask the children to tell you the pronouns in each paragraph. Underline them.
- ✦ Now explain that the writing was written by someone who didn't actually know Alex and he had assumed that he was a boy, but in fact Alex is a girl! What would the author need to do in order to correct the text so it could be published?
- ✦ With the children's help, change 'he' to 'she', 'him' to 'her' and 'his' to 'her' throughout the text. Reread the text – is it correct now?
- ✦ Tell the children that they will now be doing the same task using an activity sheet and that you will also be showing them how they can make the same changes when using a word-processing program on the computer.

Group activities

Focus group – with the teacher

- ✦ Before the lesson, enter on the computer two extracts similar to page 66. Remind the children how they physically altered the pronouns in the text on their activity sheets. Tell them that you will show them how a computer can do this task for them automatically!
- ✦ Demonstrate how to use the 'find and replace' facilities (sometimes called 'search and replace') using one of the extracts. Make sure they are aware that they need to tell the computer to find whole words only. Show them what happens if they do not. For example, if you replace 'her' with 'his' and do not select whole words only, the word 'brother' might be altered to 'brothis'!
- ✦ Ask the children to use 'find and replace' in the second extract and print out their work.

Note: To make your extract more memorable for the children, write a short story about a monster. Allow the children to replace 'the monster' with your name (for example, Mrs Jones). This is guaranteed to entertain the children and help them remember how to use 'find and replace'!

Using the photocopiable activity sheets

- ✦ Use the sheets before the computer session.

Plenary session

Share the responses to the activity sheets. Did everyone find all the pronouns to change? Compare this task with using the computer – what advantages are there? Does the computer save time? Does it eliminate the possibility of missing words? How useful would it be in a very large document if one word needed to be changed throughout? What can go wrong when using 'find and replace'?

Name ____________________ **Activity 1** Date ____________________

✦ All about Pat ✦

✦ The sentences below are all about a boy called Pat but unfortunately, the author thought Pat was a girl! Change all the underlined words to the correct pronoun.

Hint:	change 'she' to 'he' change 'her' to 'him' or 'his'

1 Pat lives with <u>her</u> family in Northern Ireland.

2 <u>She</u> loves animals so much that <u>she</u> wants to work with animals when <u>she</u> grows up.

3 Pat knows that many animals in the world are endangered and <u>her</u> greatest wish is to be able to help them.

4 Pat's brother often takes <u>her</u> to the local museum where <u>she</u> can find out about animals that live in <u>her</u> area.

5 One day Pat would love to travel to Africa where <u>she</u> might be able to see <u>her</u> favourite animal, the mountain gorilla.

6 Pat has lots of books about animals. <u>She</u> keeps them in <u>her</u> bookcase in <u>her</u> bedroom.

7 Pat writes about animals <u>she</u> sees in <u>her</u> animal journal. <u>She</u> hopes that one day <u>she</u> will use <u>her</u> notes to write a book.

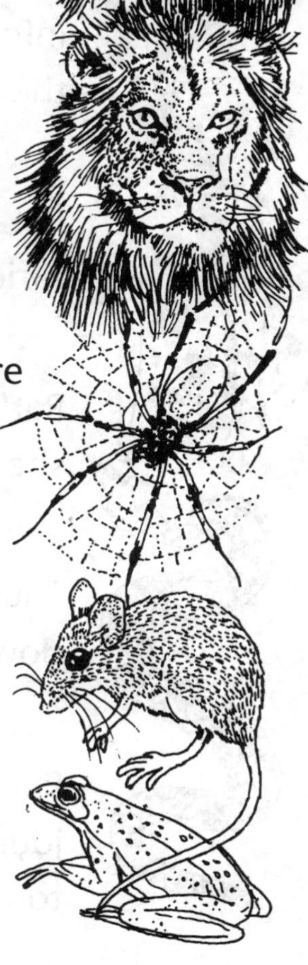

Name ______________________ **Activity 2** **Date** ______________________

✦ All about Pat ✦

✦ The passage below is all about a boy called Pat but unfortunately, the author thought Pat was a girl! Change all the pronouns in the passage. The first ones have been done for you.

his   He
Pat lives with h~~e~~r family in Northern Ireland. S~~h~~e loves animals so much that s~~h~~e wants to work with them when s~~h~~e leaves school.
he   he

Pat knows that many animals in the world are endangered and her greatest wish is to be able to help them.

She uses her CD-Rom encyclopaedia to find out information about animals. Her favourite animal is the mountain gorilla.

Pat hopes that one day she will be able to travel to Africa to see the animals she loves so much.

Pat's brother often takes her to their local museum so she can find out about the animals that live in her area.

Pat really enjoys watching the dipper that bobs up and down on rocks in a stream near her house.

Pat writes about the animals she sees in her animal journal. She hopes that one day she will use her notes to write a book.

Name ____________________ **Activity 3** **Date** ____________________

✦ All about Pat ✦

✦ The passage below is all about a boy called Pat but unfortunately, the author thought Pat was a girl! Correct all the pronouns in the passage.

Pat lives with her family in Northern Ireland. She is absolutely mad keen on animals and would love to work with animals in some way when she leaves school.

Pat is aware that many animals in the world are endangered so she has tried to find out how she can help them. She uses her CD-Rom encyclopaedia to find out information about each animal. Her favourite animal is the mountain gorilla and one day she hopes that she will be able to travel to Africa to see the gorillas in their natural habitat for herself.

Pat's brother often takes her to their local museum so she can find out about the animals that live in her area. She has discovered that there are many more animals living nearby than she first thought. One in particular really fascinates her. It is the dipper that she has been lucky enough to watch bobbing up and down on rocks in a stream near her house.

Pat writes about all the animals she sees in her animal journal. She keeps a record of when and where she saw them and makes a quick sketch. She hopes that one day she will use her notes to write a book about the animals of Northern Ireland.

Lesson 5

Creating repeating patterns

Learning objectives

- ✦ To understand that pictures/designs can be created by repeating elements.
- ✦ To create repeating patterns.
- ✦ To use stamps and/or the copy tool in a computer graphics package.
- ✦ To use the 'save as' facility to keep draft designs.

Resources

- ✦ Photocopiable pages 67 and 68.
- ✦ A computer graphics package.

Whole class introduction

- ✦ Enlarge pages 67 and 68 or make photocopies for each child or pair. Tell the children that today they will be looking at the use of patterns. Share page 67. What do they notice about the pictures? What part of each design is repeated? Do they like the effect that is created? Why/why not? How do they think the artist made sure the pattern repeated itself exactly? Discuss possible methods, such as tracing, using moulds and block printing.
- ✦ Share ideas about why an artist or designer may want to use a repeating pattern. Is it pleasing to look at? Does it take less time than using a design that does not repeat? Is it a method that has been used for centuries and is therefore familiar to us? Is it mimicking nature in any way?
- ✦ Talk about where repeating patterns might be used, both in the past (beginning with those on page 67) and in the present – vases, clothing and furniture fabrics, architraves, wallpapers, wrapping papers and book borders, such as those on page 68.
- ✦ Tell the children that you would like them to experiment with using repeating patterns themselves. Explain that they will be using an activity sheet as well as a computer program to do this. Explain the tasks on each activity sheet and discuss the effect of adding to the pattern colours that repeat.

Group activities

Focus group – with the teacher

- ✦ Show the children how to use rubber stamps and/or the copy tool in a graphics package. Ask them to spend a few minutes making a colourful abstract design. Remind them how to use the 'undo' command to go back to a previous step if a colour or pattern is unsuccessful. Remind them also that 'undo' must be the next choice directly after making the 'error'. (You cannot use 'undo' several choices later.)
- ✦ Show them the tool that allows them to do a free-form select or select within a box (this tool is often represented as a shape with a dotty outline). Ask them to choose a small area they particularly like within their picture then use the tool to select the area by pressing down the mouse button and dragging. Then ask them to do the following:
  - – go to edit menu, select 'cut'
  - – go to file and select 'new' (do not save changes to untitled work)
  - – on a new page, go to edit, select 'paste' (every time 'paste' is selected the image will be pasted again).

  They can then use the mouse to click, drag and place the images where they want them.
- ✦ Demonstrate how to use the 'save as' command to save different versions of the design.
- ✦ Ask the children to print out their final version.

Using the photocopiable activity sheets

- ✦ The sheets could be used before or after the computer session.

Plenary session

Share the work. Ask the children to consider the advantages /disadvantages of using the computer to produce their pattern. Which method is more accurate – hand or computer? Which provides more options? What uses can they suggest for the graphics program? Who do they think might use it, for example in industry?

Name ____________ **Activity 1** Date ____________

✦ Repeating patterns ✦

✦ Complete these patterns by repeating them. Colour them in.

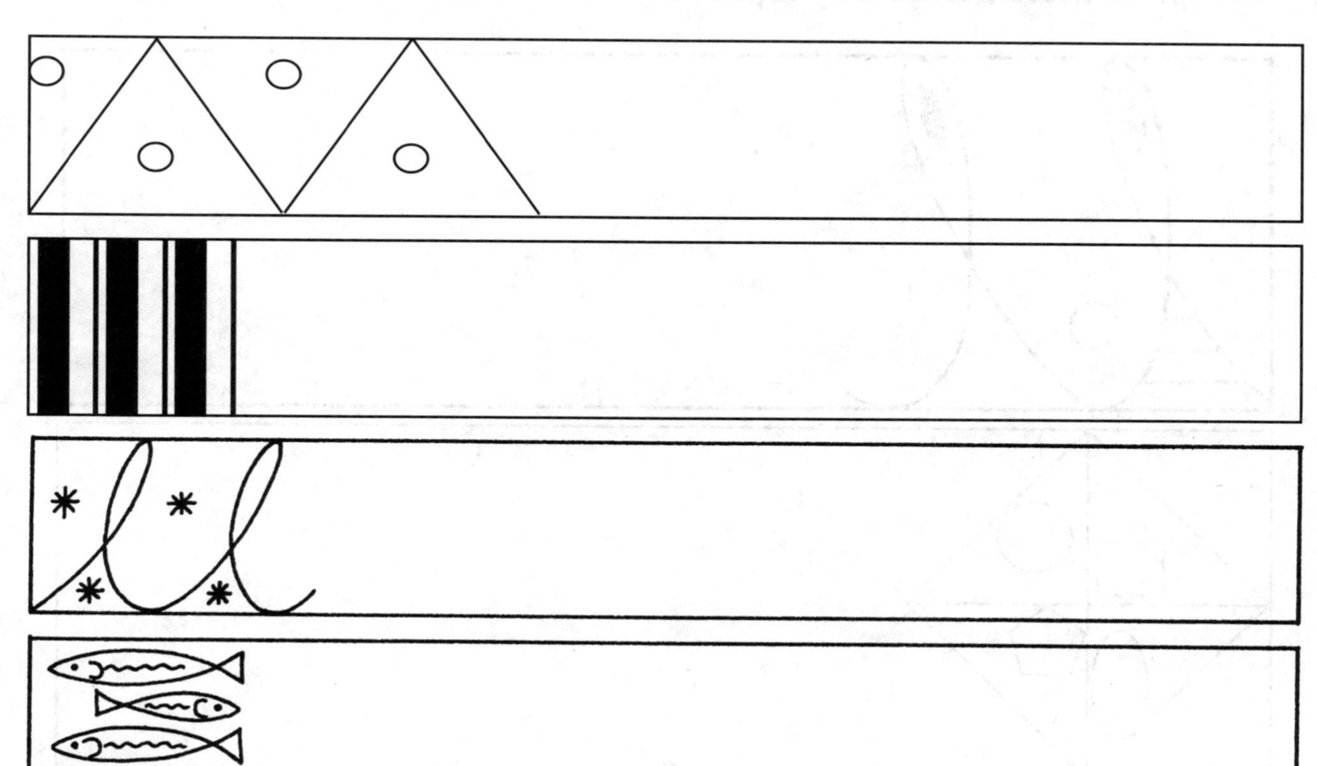

✦ Now draw and colour three repeating patterns of your own.

Name ______________ **Activity 2** Date ______________

✦ Repeating patterns ✦

✦ Complete these patterns by repeating them. Colour them in.

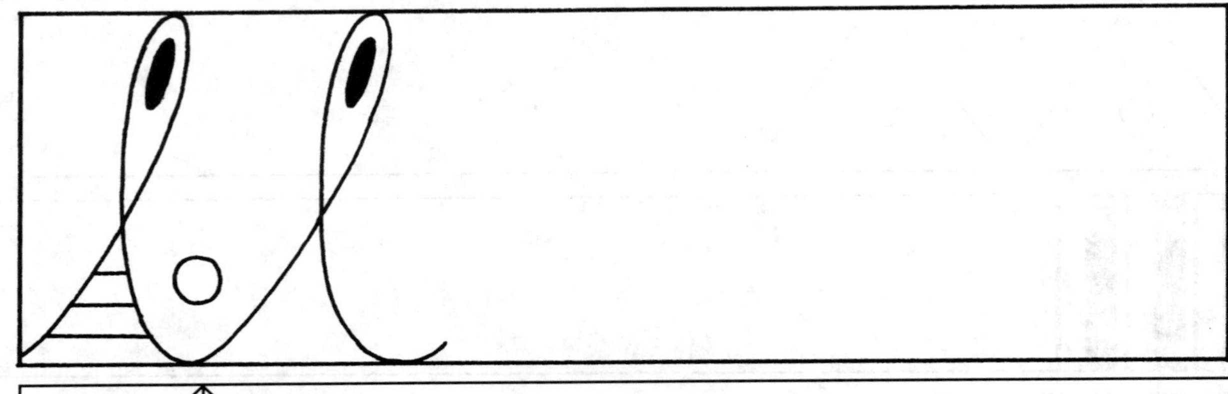

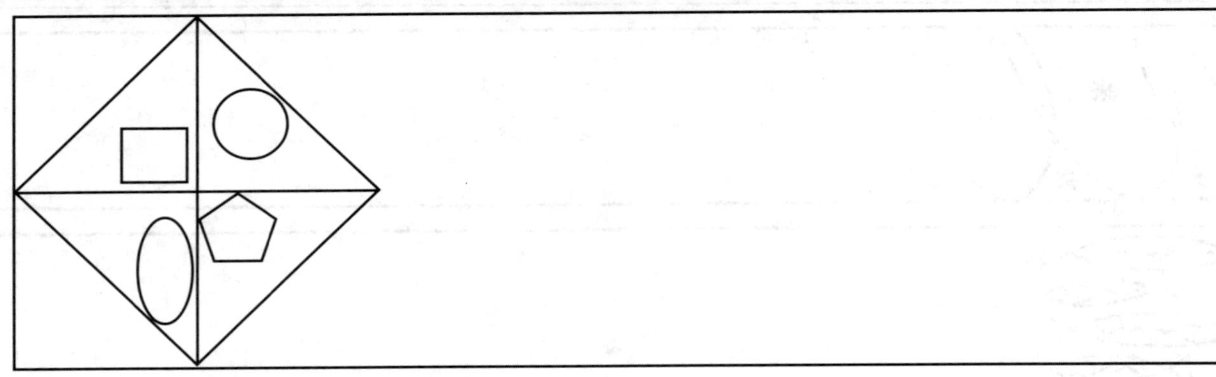

✦ Now draw and colour two repeating patterns of your own.

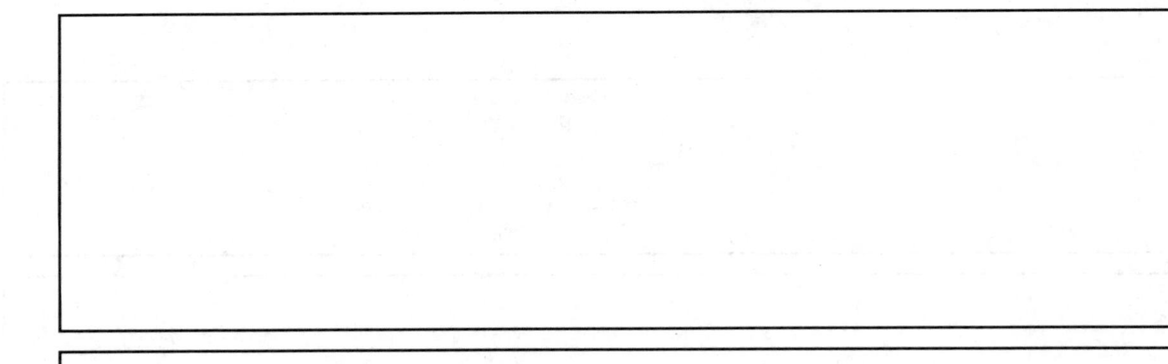

Name ______________________ **Activity 3** **Date** ______________________

✦ Repeating patterns ✦

✦ Complete these patterns by repeating them. Colour them in.

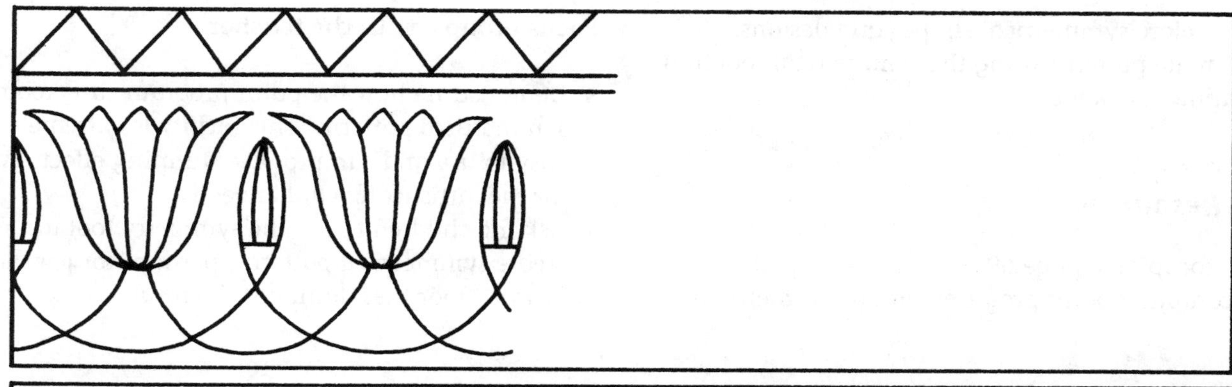

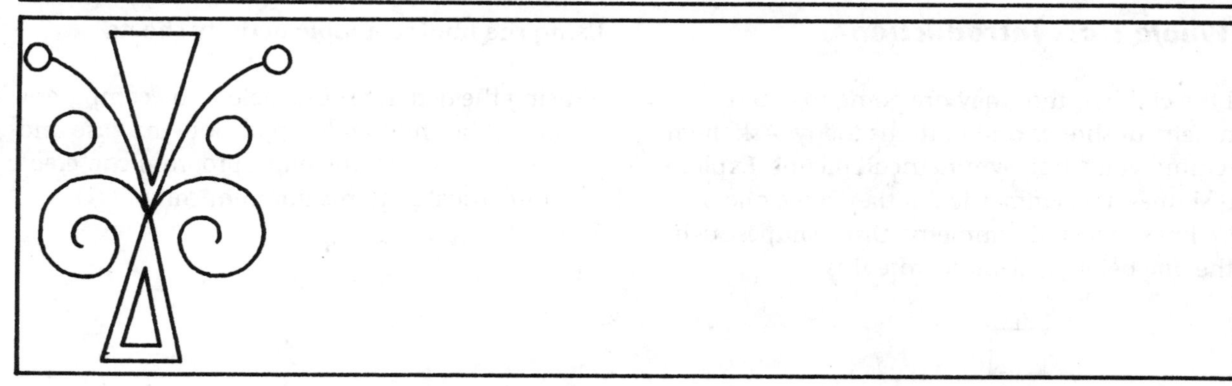

✦ Now draw and colour two repeating patterns of your own.

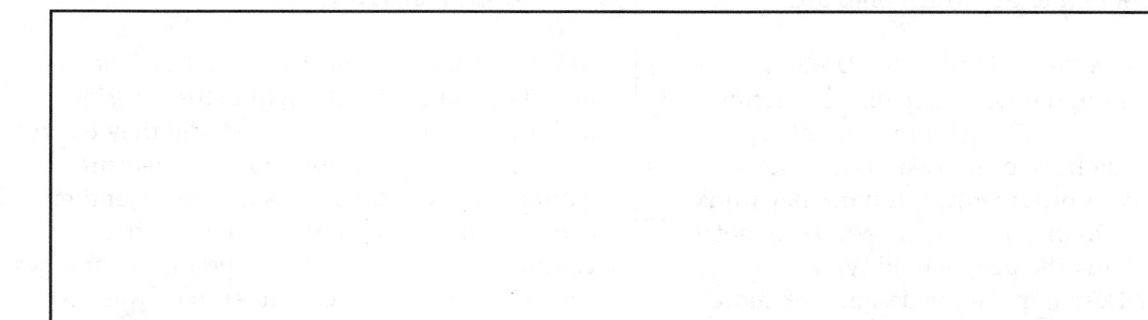

Using symmetry

Learning objectives

- To explore symmetrical shapes and designs.
- To create patterns using the symmetrical tool in a graphics package.

Resources

- Photocopiable page 69.
- A computer paint program with a symmetry tool.

Whole class introduction

- Tell the children that they are going to explore symmetrical shapes and patterns today. Ask them to remind you what 'symmetrical' means. Explain that shapes are symmetrical if they have one or more lines (axes) of symmetry. Draw shapes such as the one below to demonstrate this:

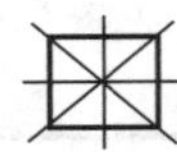

- Ask the children to explore symmetry themselves for a few minutes by getting them to draw letters of the alphabet to find out which ones are symmetrical.
- Show them the patterns on page 69. Do they think these are symmetrical? Explain that some of the patterns are Ancient Egyptian and Celtic designs that may have been used to decorate walls, jewellery or ornaments. What do they think of the designs? Do they like them? Why/why not? Why do they think the people used symmetry in their designs? Does it make the design look more structured and ordered? Explain that sometimes the designers took their inspiration from nature and copied plants and animals that were symmetrical.
- Tell the children that they are going to create some symmetrical shapes and patterns themselves now, using an activity sheet as well as a computer program.

Group activities

Focus group – with the teacher

- Demonstrate how the paint program can create symmetrical patterns. This facility is extremely easy to use and can produce stunning effects even for the 'artistically-challenged'!
- Ask the children to use the symmetry tool to create symmetrical patterns, perhaps for jewellery or wall/floor tiles. Print out the results.

Using the photocopiable activity sheets

- Using the activity sheets before the computer will enable the children to appreciate the ease and speed with which the paint program can create symmetrical patterns automatically.

Plenary session

Ask the children to share the results of their activity sheets. Were the symmetrical designs difficult to copy? What methods did they try to help them? Did they use a ruler to measure, for example? How difficult was it to think of their own design? Compare this activity to the computer task. What advantages/disadvantages were there in using a computer to do this task? Did it free the children to think more creatively about the end design? Did it provide them with options not possible when hand-drawing a design? Which end result is more accurate? Which end result is better presented? Which end results are the children most pleased with? Why? What uses can they think of for the computer drawing program? Who might use it and for what purpose?

Name ____________________ **Activity 1** Date ____________________

✦ Symmetrical patterns ✦

✦ Make these shapes symmetrical by drawing the other half. Colour them in.

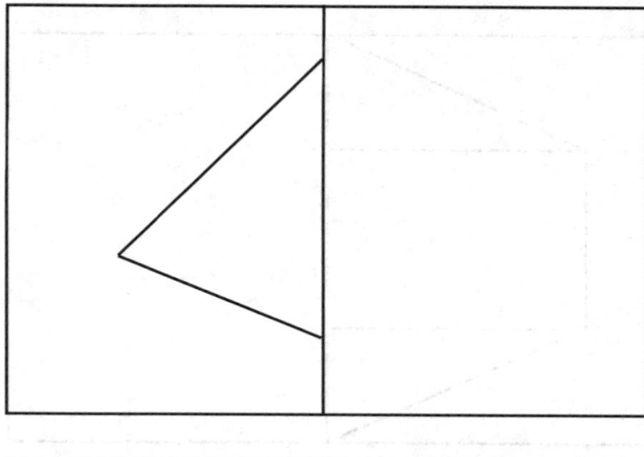
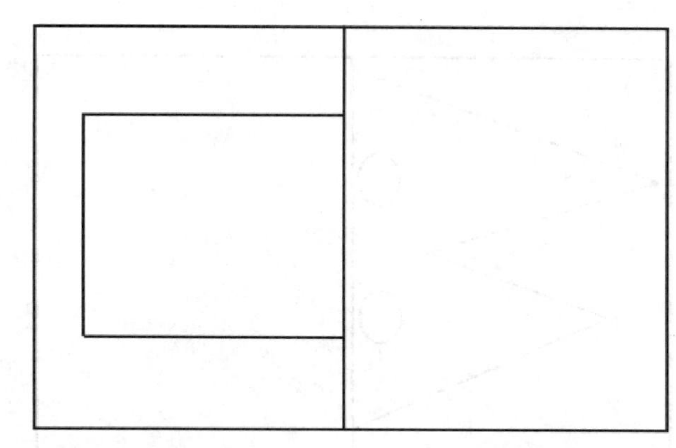
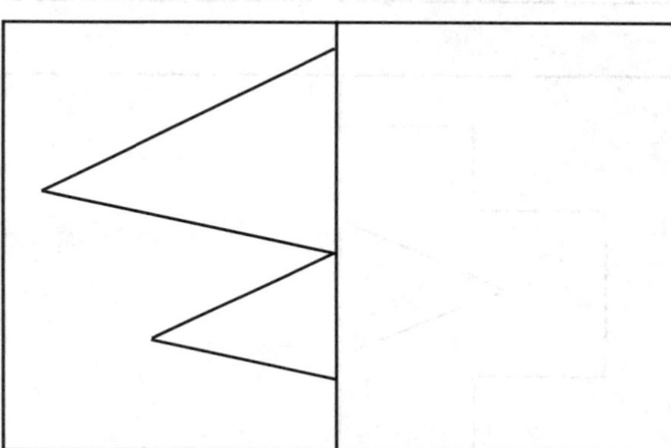
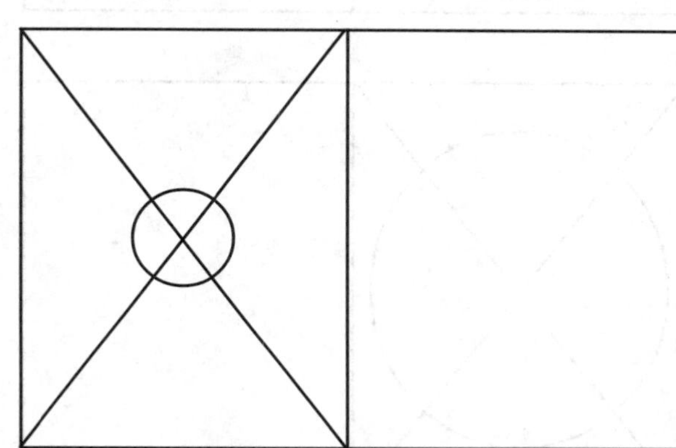

✦ Now draw and colour your own symmetrical pattern in the space below.

Name ____________________ **Activity 2** **Date** ____________________

✦ Symmetrical patterns ✦

✦ Make these shapes symmetrical by drawing the other half. Colour them in.

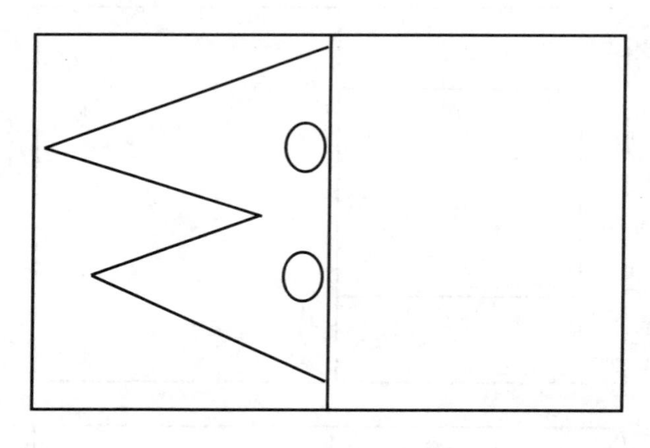

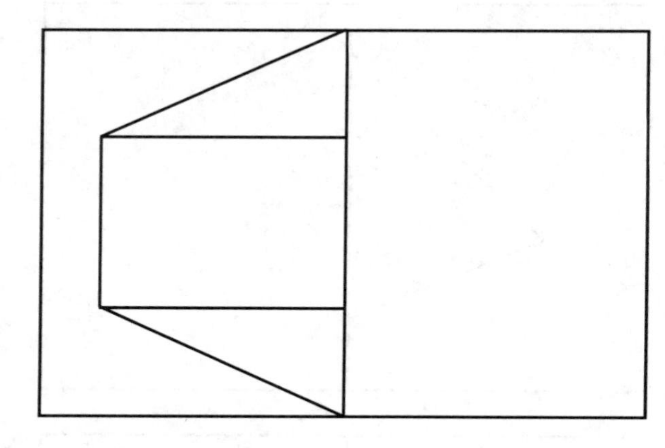

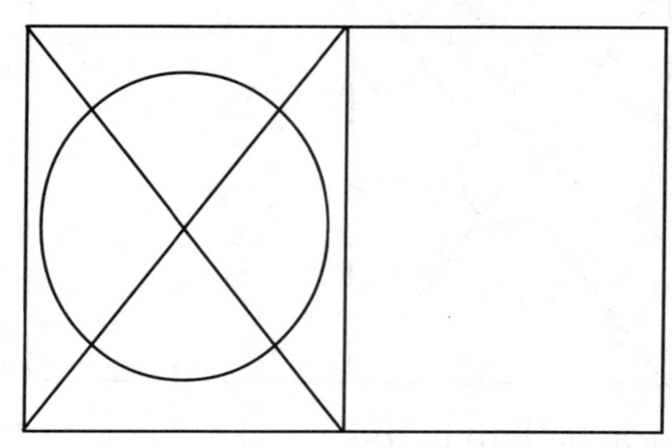

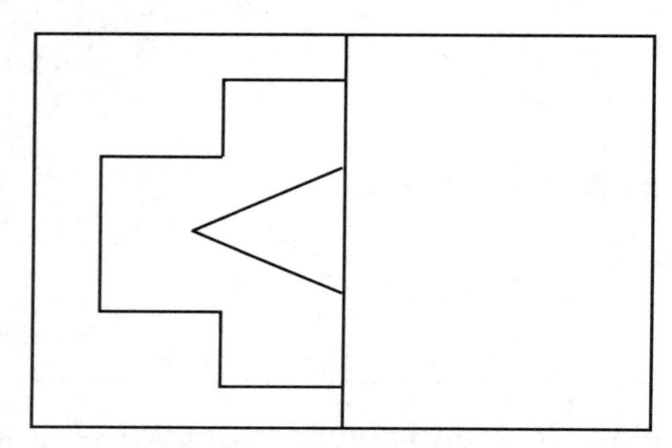

✦ Now draw and colour your own symmetrical pattern in the space below.

Name ____________________ **Activity 3** **Date** ____________________

✦ Symmetrical patterns ✦

✦ Make these shapes symmetrical by drawing the other half.
Colour them in.

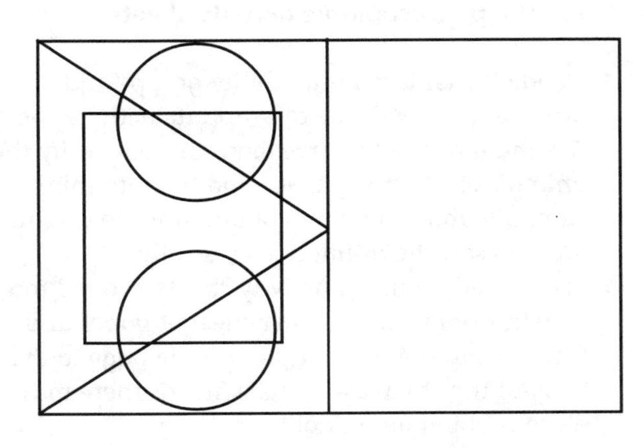

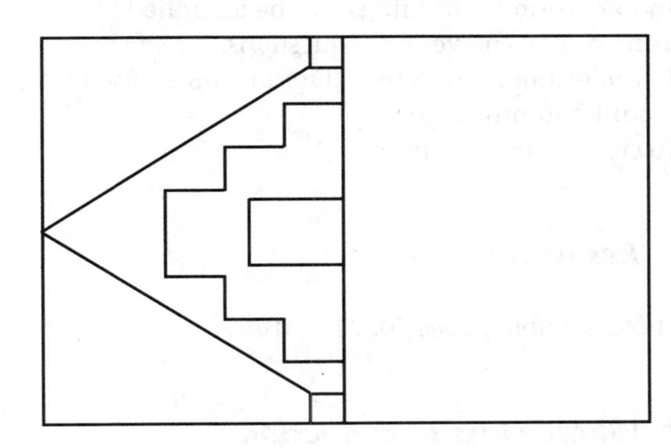

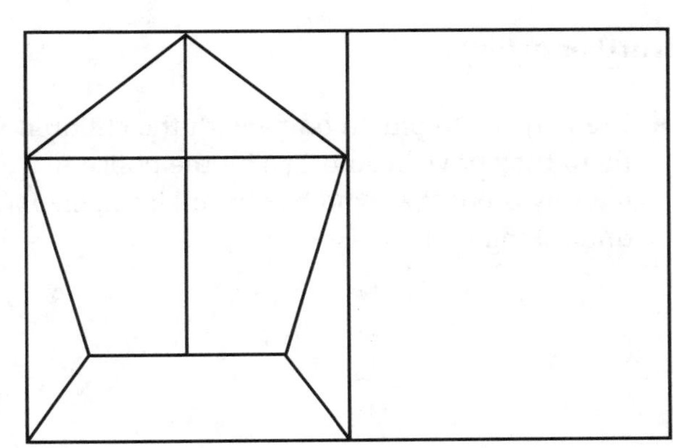

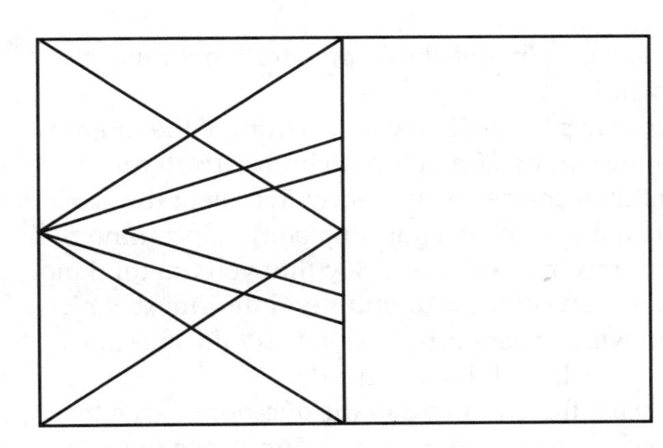

✦ Now draw and colour your own symmetrical pattern in the space below.

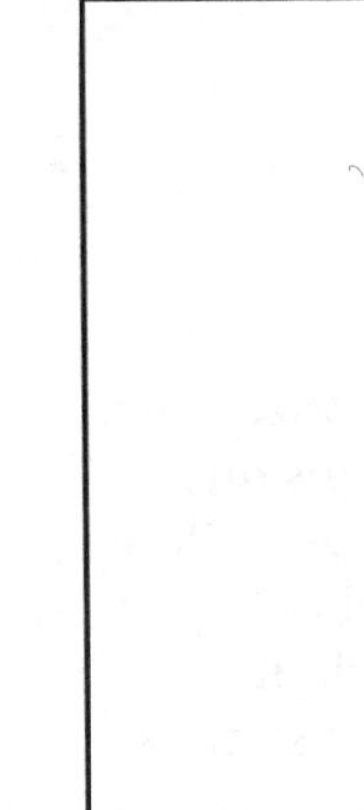

Lesson 7

Tree diagrams

Learning objectives

- ✦ To understand that things can be identified by using a series of 'yes'/'no' questions.
- ✦ To understand that a tree diagram can be used to organise information.
- ✦ To create a tree diagram.

Resources

- ✦ Photocopiable pages 70, 71 and 72.

Whole class introduction

This lesson is intended as a preparation for using a branching database program.

- ✦ Enlarge page 70. Show the pictures of the animals to the children and place them where all the children can see them clearly. Tell them that you are going to play a guessing game concerning the animals in the pictures. Say that you are thinking of just one of these animals and they must work out which one it is by asking 'yes'/'no' questions, such as 'Does it have wings?'
- ✦ Discuss the usefulness of the questions asked to help them guess the animal. Encourage them to use questions that will divide the animals into two groups, such as 'Does it have legs?'. Explain that it is unhelpful to ask questions where the answer is always going to be 'no' or where it is not possible to tell the answer from the picture, for example 'Does it make a noise?'.
- ✦ Repeat the game to identify another animal. What is the least number of questions that can be asked to obtain the correct answer?
- ✦ Tell the children that the questions they have asked can be recorded in a special way called a tree diagram. Draw an example tree diagram for these animals on the board (refer to page 71). Make sure the children understand how the tree diagram works by starting at the top of the diagram and answering the questions to identify each animal.
- ✦ Tell them that they are now going to create a tree diagram of their own using some pictures of animals that are endangered species.

Group activities

Using the photocopiable activity sheets

- ✦ Divide the children into ability groups and provide them with the appropriate activity sheet. Ask them to create a tree diagram to identify the animals on their page. Remind them to think carefully about the types of questions to ask in order to sort the animals successfully.
- ✦ Some children using Activity sheets 2 and 3 may benefit from using a larger sheet of paper and transferring the information on the page to that. Suggest that they use pencils first as there may be some rubbing out to do!

Further activity

- ✦ Use page 72 to play a game with the children. Tell them they have been asked by the police to identify a poacher who has been killing elephants and taking their tusks.

Plenary session

Share the responses to the activity sheets. Is it possible to have different questions and still categorize each picture separately? How important is it to think carefully about the right questions to ask? You may find it appropriate to tell the children that scientists use tree diagrams to classify things. You could show the children a plant or animal identification key as an example.

Name ____________________ **Activity 1** **Date** ____________________

✦ A tree diagram ✦

✦ Complete this tree diagram for the animals below. Then cut out each picture and glue it in the correct place.

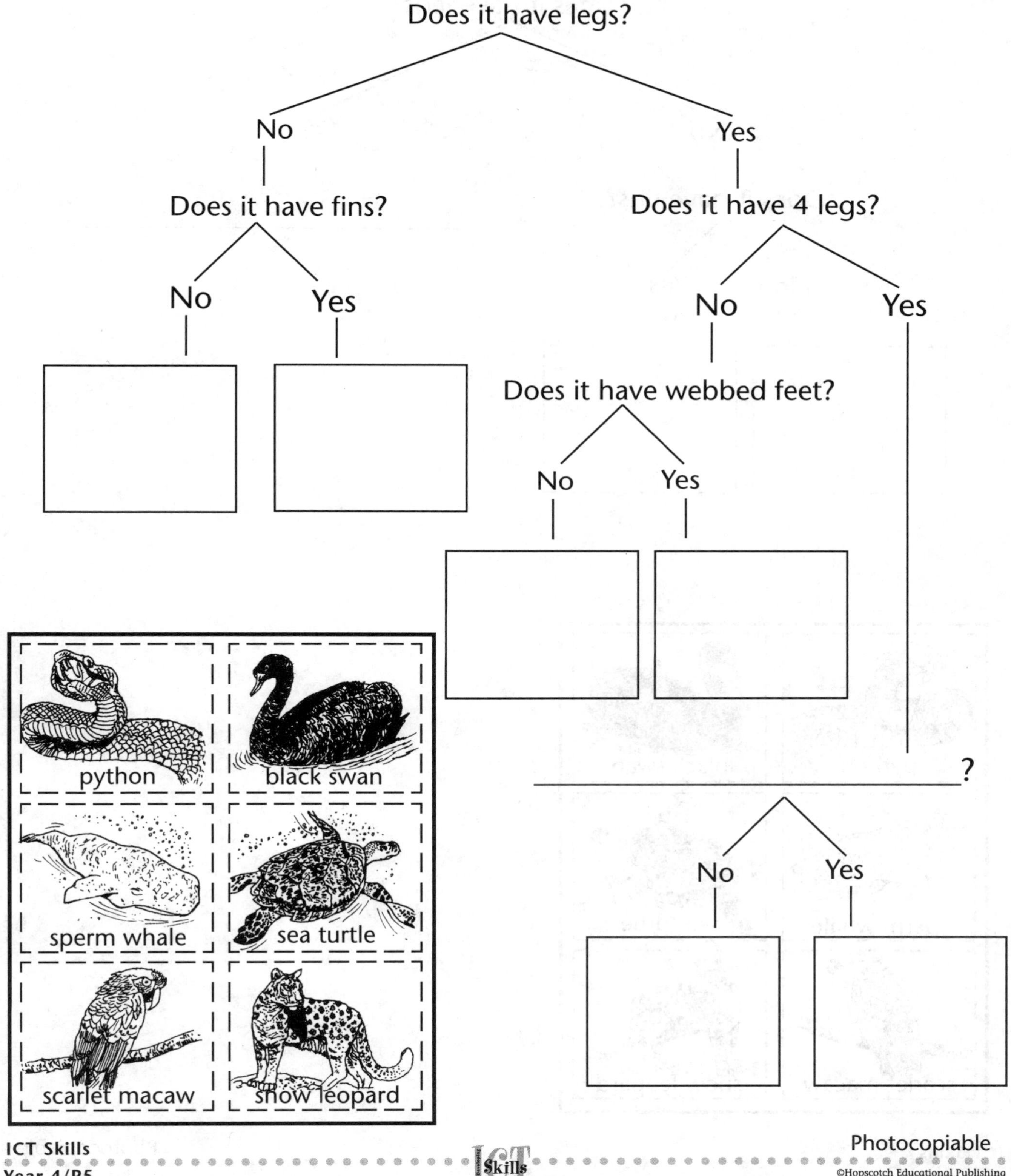

Name ____________ **Activity 2** Date ____________

✦ A tree diagram ✦

✦ Complete this tree diagram for the animals below. Then cut out each picture and glue it in the correct place.

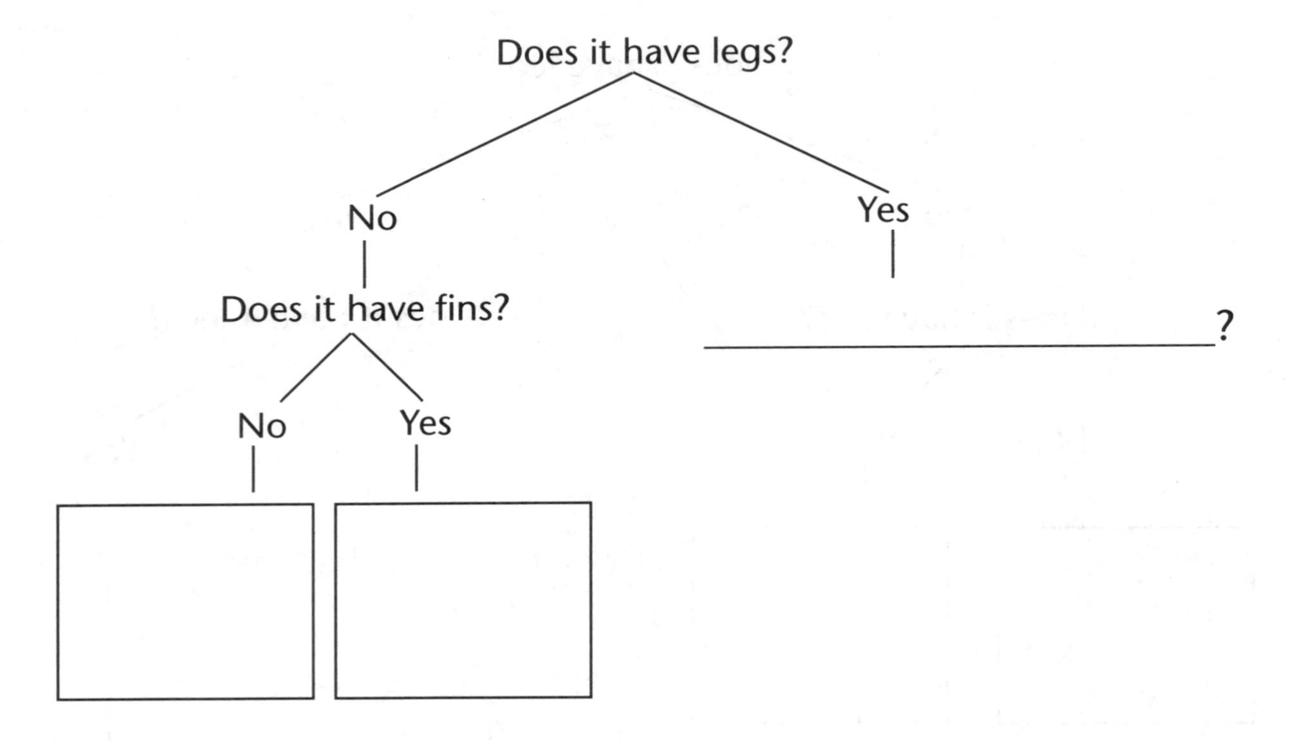

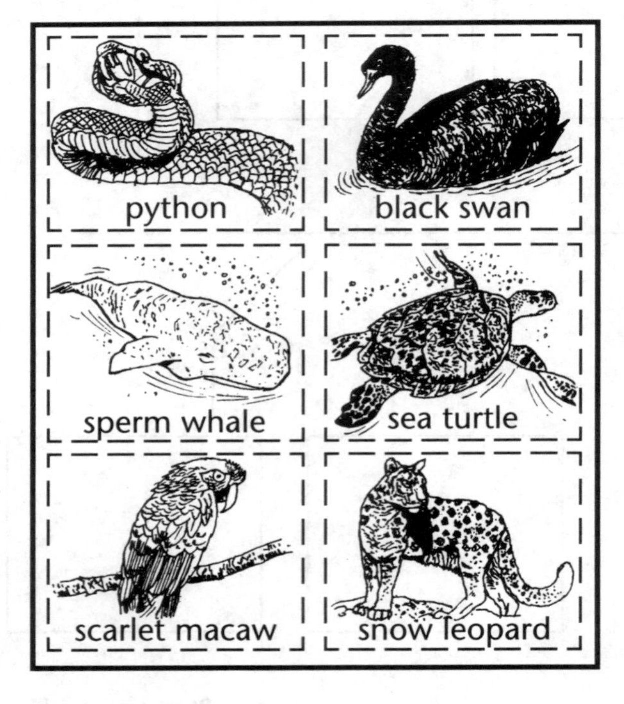

Name ____________________ Activity 3 Date ____________________

✦ A tree diagram ✦

✦ Create a tree diagram for the animals below by writing suitable questions. Then cut out each picture and glue it in the correct place.

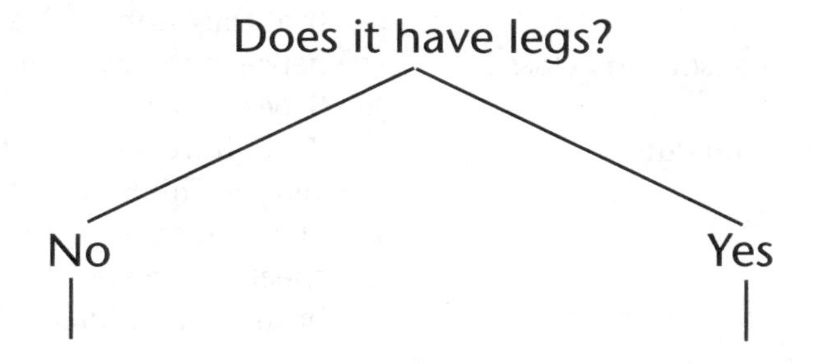

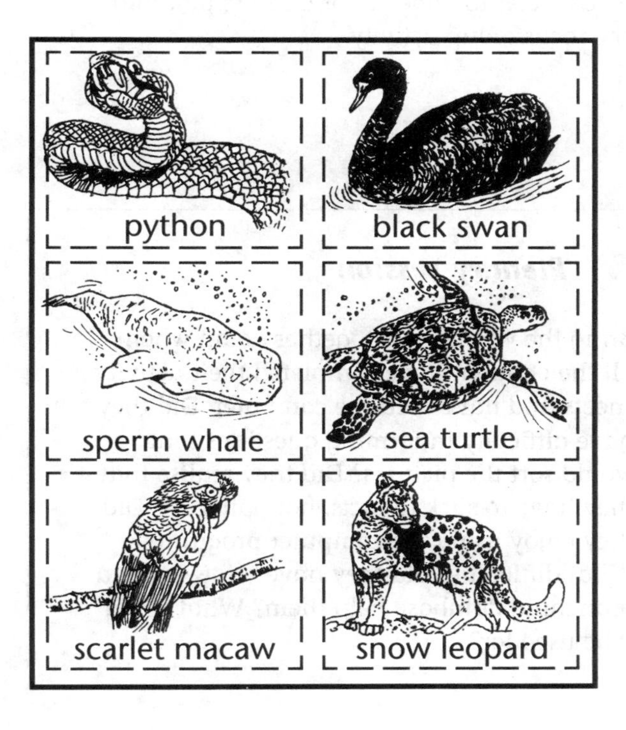

Lesson 8

Branching databases

Learning objectives

- To understand that information can be sorted and classified.
- To know that ICT can be used to sort and classify information.
- To create and search a branching database.

Resources

- Photocopiable page 73.
- Pictures of a pushchair, bicycle, plane and sailboat.
- A branching database program.

Whole class introduction

- Tell the children that they will be learning how to use a branching database program on the computer. Say that in order to know how the program works, they will be doing some activities first. Explain that the program they are going to use will be comparing different types of transport. Can they name some types of transport? Write a list of them on the board, making sure you include the four types in the pictures as listed in Resources above.
- Tell the children that you are going to choose two of these and hold up the pictures of the pushchair and the bicycle. Tell them that you want them to think of 'yes'/'no' questions that they could ask about the pictures. Write the questions on the board, for example:

  Does it have wheels?
  Can you push it?
  Does it carry people?
  Can it carry parcels?
  Does it cause pollution?
  Do you pedal it?
  Can you steer it?
- Now ask the children to look at the questions and choose one(s) that they think will sort them into two sets. (That is, the question that will give a 'yes' to one of the pictures and a 'no' to the other one.) In this example it will be the question 'Do you pedal it?'
- Do the same with the pictures of the plane and the sail-boat. You may like the children to work in pairs to see if they can come up with a question that they think will sort out the difference between the two. The questions might include: 'Does it fly in the air?','Does it have sails?' or 'Does it travel on water?'
- Tell the children that they are now going to think of some more sorting questions using an activity sheet before you show them how to use the branching database program on the computer.

Group activities

Using the photocopiable activity sheets

- Ask the children to complete the sheets before carrying out the focus group work.
- Divide them into ability groups and provide them with the appropriate activity sheet. Remind those children using Activity sheets 2 and 3 to write 'yes'/'no' type questions.

Focus group – with the teacher

- Please refer to page 73 for a full explanation of the focus group activity.

Plenary session

Bring the whole class together again when all the children have completed their activity sheets and have used the computer. Did they have difficulty in forming questions that would sort the pictures? Did they realise that they have to stick to facts, not opinions? Did they enjoy using the computer program? What difficulties did they have? How could a branching database help them? What could it be used for?

Name ____________________ **Activity 1** **Date** ____________________

✦ Questions, questions! ✦

✦ Tick the correct question that would help sort out the difference between each type of transport below.

1

Can it travel faster than a horse? ☐

Does it run on rails? ☐

Does it carry people? ☐

Does it have a driver? ☐

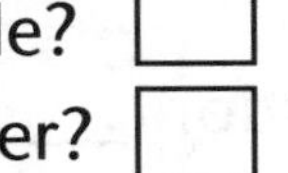

2

Can it travel on water? ☐

Can it travel under water? ☐

Does it carry people? ☐

Does it have an engine? ☐

3

Can it be used by just 1 person? ☐

Does it have wheels? ☐

Can it carry parcels? ☐

Does it cause pollution? ☐

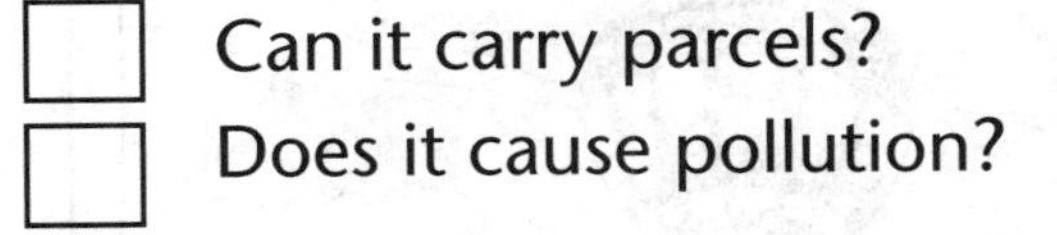

✦ Now write your own question that would help sort out the difference between a plane and a boat.

Name ____________________ **Activity 2** **Date** ____________________

✦ Questions, questions! ✦

✦ Write questions that would help sort out the difference between each type of transport below.

For example: car and train

Question: Does it run on rails?

1

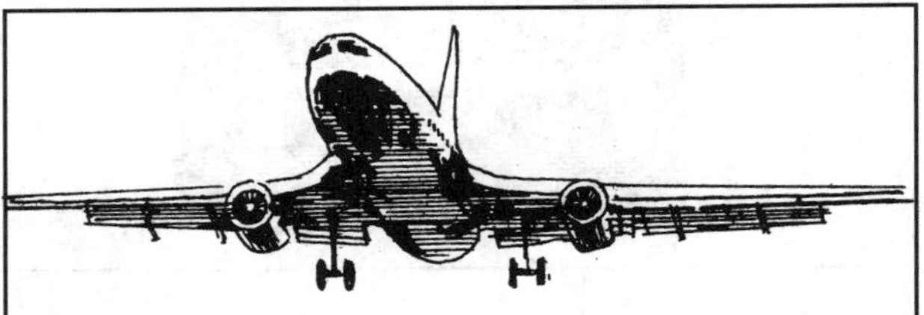

Your question: ____________________

2

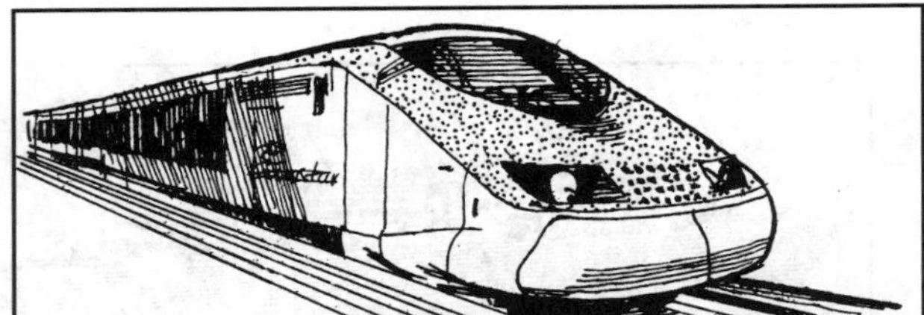

Your question: ____________________

3

Your question: ____________________

4

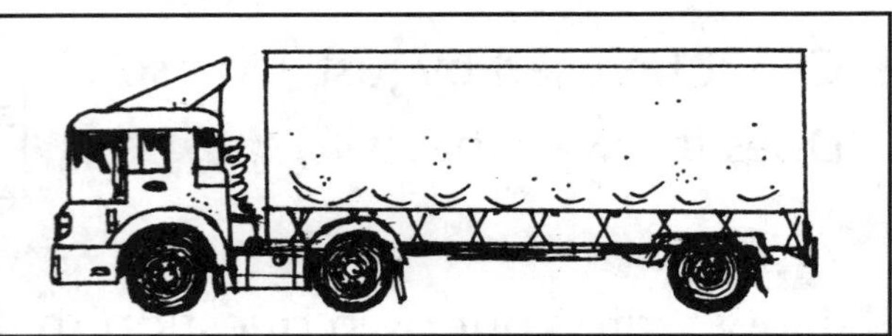

Your question: ____________________

Name ______________________ **Activity 3** **Date** ______________________

✦ Questions, questions! ✦

✦ Write questions that would help sort out the difference between each type of transport below.

1

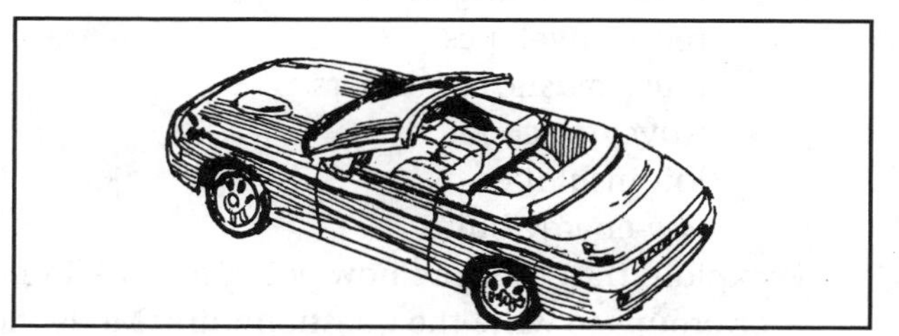

Your question: ____

2

Your question: ____

3

Your question: ____

4

Your question: ____

Questionnaires

Learning objectives

- To understand that information can be collected using a simple questionnaire.
- To design a simple questionnaire to record numbers, text and choices.
- To create a database to store the information collected from a questionnaire.

Resources

- A data-handling package.

Whole class introduction

- Remind the children what a database is. Can they remember what a record is? What is a field? Make sure they understand the terms. Tell them that they are going to produce a database about how environmentally-friendly or 'green' the homes are of the children in their class. How might such a database help us? Why might we want to find out this information?
- Tell them that they are going to write a questionnaire to find out the information they need. Have they used a questionnaire before? How important is it that each person in the class uses the same questions when finding out the information? Why?
- Remind the class that there are three types of information that can be entered in a field in a record – number, text and choice. Remind them also that a computer can only treat things the same if they are called by the same name, so it is important to agree on what type of information each field will contain. Discuss how much easier it would be to enter the information into the database if the questions matched the fields in each record.
- Write the following fields on the board:

  family name
  number of adults
  number of children
  number of cars
  number of bicycles
  recycle paper
  recycle cans
  recycle bottles
  recycle clothing
  recycle plastic
  recycle food
  reuse shopping bags
  reuse envelopes
  reuse plastic containers
  travel to school
  loft insulation
  low-energy bulbs
- Explain that they are now going to work in pairs or groups to write the questionnaire. Model how to write a question to match a field, for example:
  field: family name
  question: What is your family name?

Group activities

Using the photocopiable activity sheets

Divide the children into ability groups and provide them with the appropriate activity sheet.

Plenary session

Share the responses. What problems did they have (especially those who completed Activity sheet 3)? Do they consider that any of the questions should not be asked for reasons of privacy or confidentiality? Remind the children that we have a right not to answer questions if we do not want to and that we should think carefully about the types of information we store on computers. Agree on the final wording for each question. Ask the children to take their questionnaires home to complete them.

Follow-up session

- Help the children create a single database to store the collected information. Allow the children to enter information in pairs – one doing the data entry, the other checking for accuracy.

Name ____________________ **Activity 1** Date ____________________

✦ My questionnaire ✦

✦ You are going to write a questionnaire to find out how 'green' the homes of the people in your class are!
These are the things you need to find out:

1. The person's name and the number of adults and children living in the house
2. The number of cars and bicycles at the house
3. Whether they recycle paper, cans, bottles, plastic, clothing or food
4. Whether they reuse shopping bags, envelopes or plastic containers
5. How the children get to school – car, walk, bus, bicycle
6. Whether or not the loft is insulated
7. Whether or not they use low-energy light bulbs

✦ Some of the questionnaire has been done for you.
Complete the rest of it yourself.

Questionnaire – How 'Green' is Your Home?

1. What is your family name?____________
2. How many adults live in your house?__________
3. How many children live in your house?__________
4. How many cars do you own?_______ 5 How many bicycles?______
6. Do you recycle any of the following things?
   a) paper_______ b) cans_______ c)
   d) e) f)
7. Do you reuse any of the following things?
   a)
   b)
   c)
8. How do
9. Is the
10. Do you use

Name ____________ **Activity 2** Date ____________

✦ My questionnaire ✦

✦ You are going to write a questionnaire to find out how 'green' the homes of the people in your class are! These are the things you need to find out:

1. Person's name and number of adults and children living in the house
2. Number of cars and bicycles at the house
3. Whether they recycle paper, cans, bottles, plastic, clothing or food
4. Whether they reuse shopping bags, envelopes or plastic containers
5. How the children get to school – car, walk, bus, bicycle
6. Whether or not the loft is insulated
7. Whether or not they use low-energy light bulbs

✦ Complete the questionnaire below by writing the necessary questions.

Questionnaire – How 'Green' is Your Home?

1 What is your family name?____________

2 How many adults live in your house?____________

3 How many children live in your house?____________

4 How many cars do you own?_______ **5** How many bicycles?_____

6 Do you recycle any of the following things?

a) **b)** **c)**

d) **e)** **f)**

7

8

9

Name ______________________ Activity 3 Date ______________________

✦ My questionnaire ✦

✦ You are going to write a questionnaire to find out how 'green' the homes of the people in your class are!
These are the things you need to find out:

1. Person's name and number of adults and children living in the house
2. Number of cars and bicycles at the house
3. Whether they recycle paper, cans, bottles, plastic, clothing or food
4. Whether they reuse shopping bags, envelopes or plastic containers
5. How the children get to school – car, walk, bus, bicycle
6. Whether or not the loft is insulated
7. Whether or not they use low-energy light bulbs

✦ Write the questions for your questionnaire in the box below.

Questionnaire – How 'Green' is Your Home?

Lesson 10

Pie charts

Learning objectives

- ✦ To understand that different graphs are used for different purposes.
- ✦ To understand that pie charts can be used to make comparisons between populations.
- ✦ To use ICT to create pie charts in a data handling package.

Resources

- ✦ Photocopiable page 74.
- ✦ A data-handling package.

Whole class introduction

- ✦ Enlarge page 74. Tell the children that they are going to be working with graphs today. Show them the examples of the bar and pie charts on page 74. Explain that these charts actually show the same information but in a different way. Look at the bar-graphs first. Remind the children how they are constructed – with the number (in this case 'children') on the vertical axis and the subject (in this case 'type of transport') along the horizontal axis. Remind them that a graph also has an appropriate title. Ask them questions about the information contained in the bar-graphs, such as 'How many children travel to school by car?', 'Which form of transport is the most common?' and 'How many more children travel by bus than cycle?'
- ✦ Now compare the pie charts with the bar-graphs. Tell the children that the charts represent the exact same information but in a way that helps us to compare the whole school results more easily with that of class 4. Discuss how difficult it is to compare the two bar-graphs when one is much larger than the other, but with the pie charts, you can compare the two distributions more easily because the larger the section of the chart, the larger the proportion of children it represents. So although it is not as easy to work out exactly how many children travel to school using the different forms of transport, it is much more useful for making comparisons.
- ✦ If appropriate, explain how the charts are constructed – ie a circle equals 360° and the segments represent a fraction of the circle. For most children, however, it is sufficient for them to know how to compare the relative sizes of the segments by referring to approximate fractions of the circle.
- ✦ Ask the children questions about the information contained in the pie charts.

Group activities

Using the photocopiable activity sheets

- ✦ Use the activity sheets immediately after the introductory session to assess how well the children can interpret pie charts.

Follow-up session

- ✦ Invite the children to compare their own class's forms of travelling to school with the school on page 74 by asking them to collect the information and enter it into a data handling package to produce some bar and pie charts. If you don't want them to find out how children in other classes travel to school, they could test the hypothesis (for their own class) that more boys cycle to school than girls, for example.

Plenary session

Share the answers to the activity sheets. Did they have any problems interpreting the charts? Discuss the computer activity. Did the results support or reject the hypothesis? How did their own class results compare with the school on page 74? Ask questions about the pie charts produced to assess how well the children can interpret them. How useful is it to have a database program that can produce different graphs? How does this help us in using and interpreting the information gathered?

Name ____________ **Activity 1** Date ____________

✦ Pie charts ✦

✦ Use the pie charts to answer the questions.

Type of houses we live in – Redburn Primary

Class 4S – 28 children

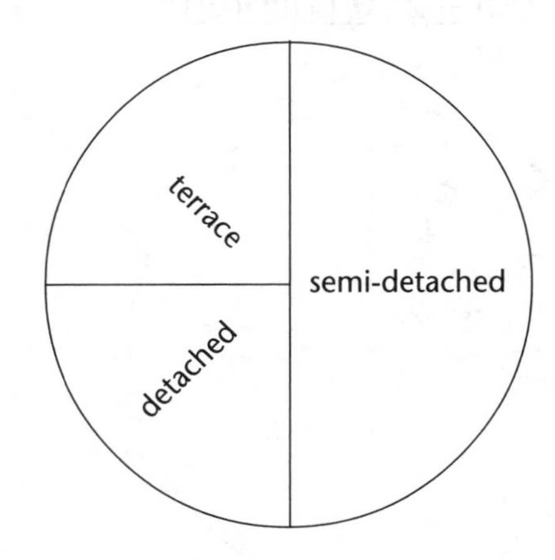

School – 200 children

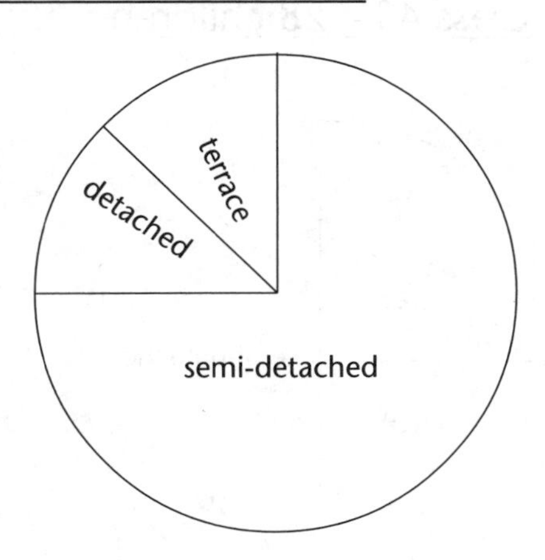

✦ Tick the correct answer.

1 Half the children in Class 4S live in terraces. ☐

Half the children in Class 4S live in semi-detached houses. ☐

2 Most children in the school live in semi-detached houses. ☐

Most children in the school live in detached houses. ☐

3 6 children in Class 4S live in detached houses. ☐

7 children in Class 4S live in detached houses. ☐

4 A third of the children in the school live in terraces. ☐

An eighth of the children in the school live in terraces. ☐

Name ____________________ **Activity 2** **Date** ____________________

✦ Pie charts ✦

✦ Use the pie charts to answer the questions.

Type of house we live in - Redburn Primary

Class 4S – 28 children

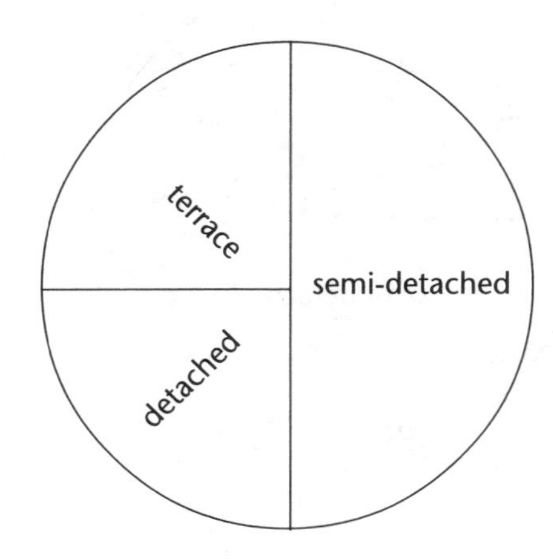

School – 200 children

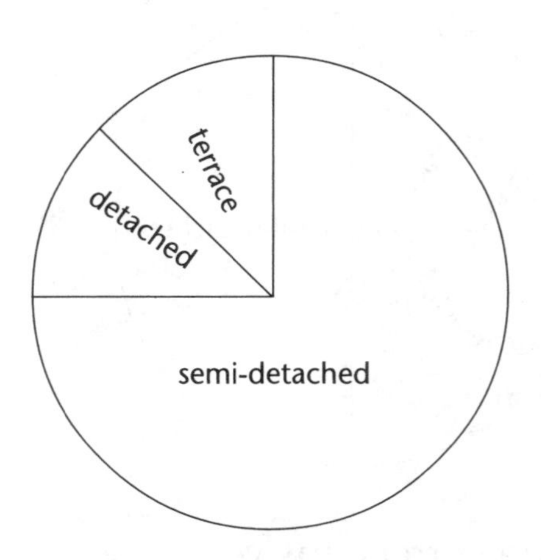

✦ Answer these questions.

1 What kind of house do most of the children in the school live in?

____

2 What fraction of Class 4S live in semi-detached houses? _________

3 What fraction of children in the school live in terraces? __________

4 How many children in Class 4S live in detached houses? _________

5 How many children in the school live in detached houses? ______

6 What fraction of the children in the school live in detached houses?

____

7 What fraction of the children in the school live in semi-detached houses?

____

8 How many children in the school live in semi-detached houses?

____

Name ____________________ **Activity 3** **Date** ____________________

✦ Pie charts ✦

✦ Use the pie charts to answer the questions.

Type of house we live in – Hilltop Primary

Class 4B – 32 children

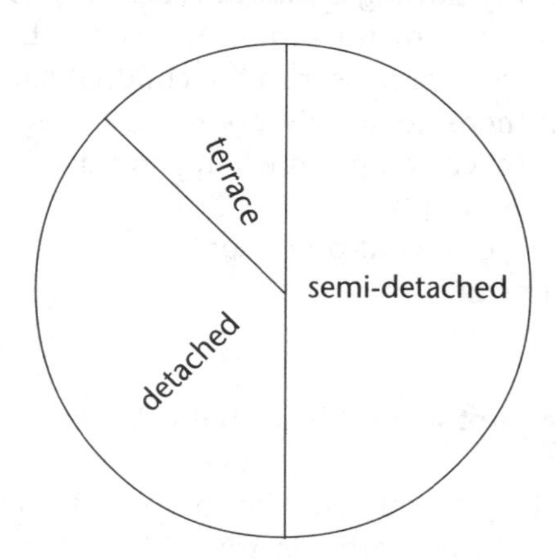

School – 288 children

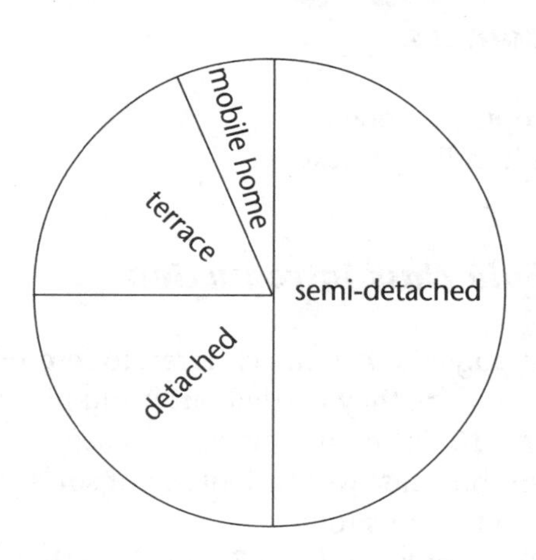

✦ Answer these questions.

1 What kind of house is the most common in Class 4B? ____________

2 How many children in Class 4B live in this kind of house? _________

3 What fraction of children in the school live in detached houses? __________

4 How many children in Class 4B live in detached houses? _________

5 How many children in the school live in detached houses? ______

6 What fraction of the children in the school live in semi-detached houses?

______________ How many children is this? ____________

7 One sixteenth of the children in the school live in mobile homes. How many children is this? ________________

8 How many children in Class 4B live in terraces? ______________

9 How many children in the school live in semi-detached and detached houses?

____

Line graphs

Learning objectives

- To understand that different graphs are used for different purposes.
- To understand that line graphs can be used to show continuously changing information.
- To use ICT to create line graphs in a data handling package.

Resources

- Photocopiable page 75.
- A data handling package.

Whole class introduction

- Enlarge page 75. Ask the children to remind you about the work they carried out using pie charts in Lesson 10. When are pie charts useful? Tell the children that they will be looking at some more charts and graphs today.
- Share the graphs on page 75. Explain that all the graphs on the page show the same information – the temperatures for a week in March in Sydney, Australia. Share the bar-chart first. Ask the children questions about the graph to interrogate it. Discuss how the pie chart is not clear. Is it useful in this form for this purpose? Compare the bar-chart with the bar line chart. Explain how it has been created.
- Explain how the line graph has been constructed by joining up the points at the top of each line in the bar line chart. Tell the children that because temperature is continuously changing, we can join the temperatures for each day in a continuous line (although it does not show all the temperature changes throughout the day).
- Ask the children to think of other things that could be recorded using line graphs.
- Ask them to record the daily temperatures for a week (or provide the information for them) before using the data handling program.

Group activities

Focus group - with the teacher

- Enter the temperature data into the data handling package. Ask the children to produce a pie chart, bar-chart and line graph, print them out and write a sentence about each graph.

  Note: many packages that produce graphs also allow you to copy the graph. You could then paste it into a word-processor so the children can write about it there. To do this, do the following:
  - choose 'copy' option when you have the desired graph
  - open your word-processor
  - go to edit
  - select 'paste'

Using the photocopiable activity sheets

- The activity sheets could be completed before or after using the computer. You will need to explain to children using Activity sheet 3 how sometimes several data sets can be incorporated into one line graph to make comparisons easier.

Plenary session

Share the responses to the activity sheets. Ask someone from group 3 to explain how their graph shows both cities together. Share the graphs printed from the computer. Ask some of the children to read the sentences they have written about them. Was the pie chart useful? Ask the children to tell you what type of graph/chart is best suited to representing particular information. How useful is it to have a computer able to interpret information and present the graphs for you? How difficult would it be to draw the graphs ourselves? Which one would be the most challenging? Why? When might we use such graphs – in science, for example?

Name ______________________ **Activity 1** **Date** ______________________

✦ Line graphs ✦

✦ Use the line graphs below to answer the questions.

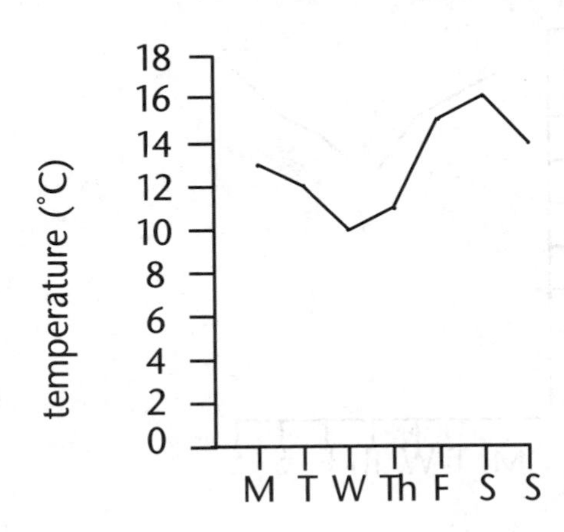

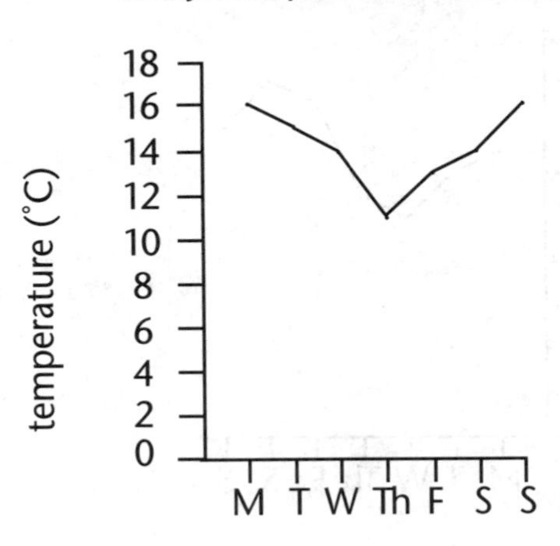

✦ Tick the correct answer. ✔

1 On Monday it was 14°C in Edinburgh. ☐
 On Monday it was 13°C in Edinburgh. ☐

2 It was 11°C in Cardiff on Thursday. ☐
 It was 10°C in Cardiff on Thursday. ☐

3 The highest temperature in Edinburgh was 18°C. ☐
 The highest temperature in Edinburgh was 16°C. ☐

4 The lowest temperature in Cardiff was 11°C. ☐
 The lowest temperature in Cardiff was 10°C. ☐

5 It was warmer in Cardiff than in Edinburgh on Sat. ☐
 It was warmer in Cardiff than in Edinburgh on Sun. ☐

6 The highest temperature for both cities was 16°C. ☐
 The highest temperature for both cities was 15°C. ☐

Name ____________ **Activity 2** **Date** ____________

✦ Line graphs ✦

✦ Use the line graphs below to answer the questions.

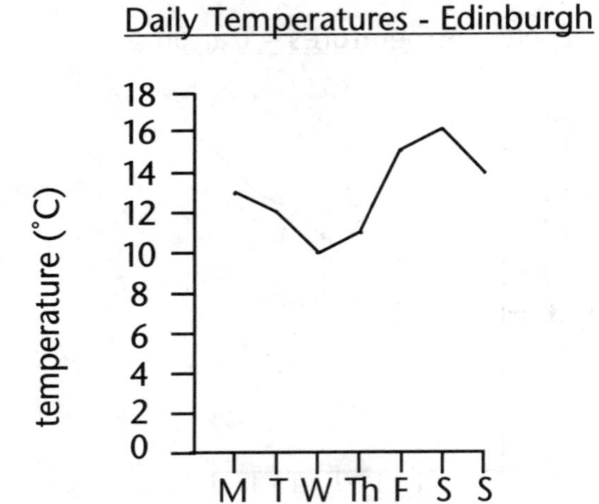

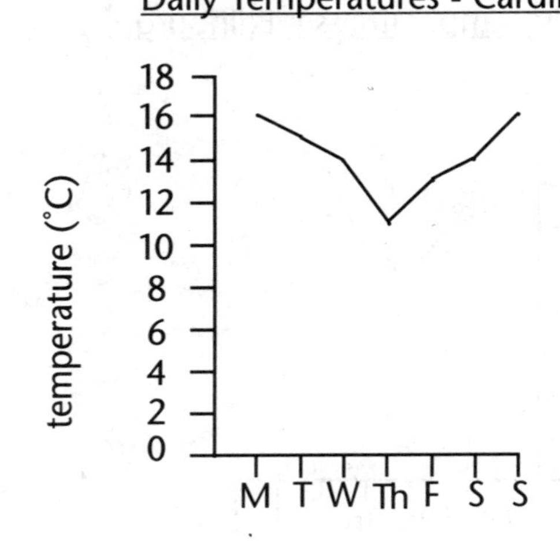

✦ Answer these questions.

1 What temperature was it in Edinburgh on Monday?____________

2 What temperature was it in Cardiff on Monday?____________

3 What temperature was it in Edinburgh on Saturday?____________

4 What temperature was it in Cardiff on Saturday?____________

5 Was it warmer in Cardiff than Edinburgh on Tuesday?____________

6 Was it cooler in Edinburgh than Cardiff on Friday?____________

7 What was the lowest temperature in Edinburgh?____________

8 What was the lowest temperature in Cardiff?____________

9 On which days was it 16 °C in Cardiff?____________

10 On what day of the week was it the same temperature in both cities?____________

11 What was the highest temperature for both cities?____________

12 Which city was coolest on Tuesday?____________

Name ____________________ **Activity 3** Date ____________________

✦ Line graphs ✦

✦ Use the line graph below to answer the questions.

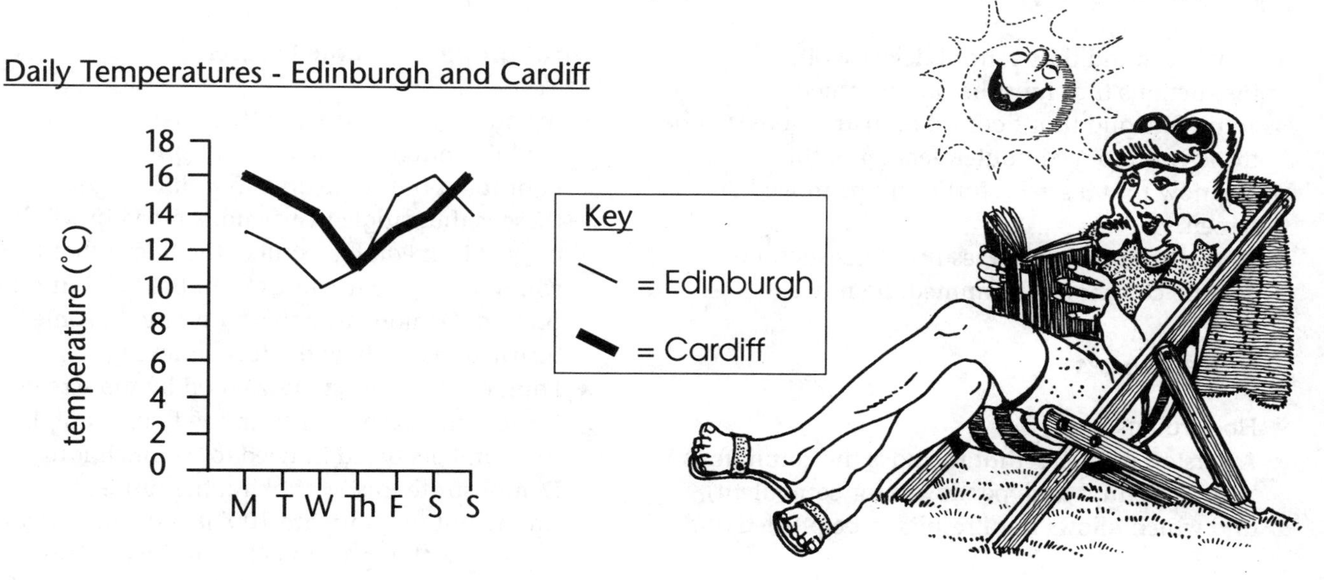

✦ Answer these questions.

1 What temperature was it in Edinburgh on Monday?____________

2 What temperature was it in Cardiff on Monday?____________

3 What temperature was it in Edinburgh on Saturday?____________

4 What temperature was it in Cardiff on Saturday?____________

5 Was it warmer in Cardiff than Edinburgh on Tuesday?____________

6 Was it cooler in Edinburgh than Cardiff on Friday?____________

7 What was the lowest temperature in Edinburgh?____________

8 What was the lowest temperature in Cardiff?____________

9 On which days was it 16 °C in Cardiff?____________

10 On what day of the week was it the same temperature in both cities?____________

11 What was the highest temperature for both cities?____________

12 Which city was coolest on Tuesday?____________

Using LOGO – introduction

Learning objectives

- ✦ To understand that control devices follow instructions that must be programmed.
- ✦ To understand that floor robot instructions can be transferred to a computer version of the robot.
- ✦ To know that a screen turtle can be moved on screen.
- ✦ To predict and test the results of instructions.
- ✦ To type commands in immediate mode.

Resources

- ✦ Floor robots.
- ✦ A version of LOGO that includes the commands 'clear', 'penup' and 'pendown' (or equivalent) and which allows final results to be printed out.

Whole class introduction

- ✦ Tell the children that they will be working with a floor robot today. Ask them to remind you what the robot can do. How does it do this? (We have to program the robot to follow instructions.) Explain that machines such as a floor robot, photocopier, video recorder or microwave must be switched on and dials and buttons pushed in a certain order before they will work. Can the children remember how to program the robot?
- ✦ Revise programming the robot by entering instructions to make it move in a square. Write the instructions on the board: forward 4 right 90 forward 4 right 90 forward 4 right 90 forward 4 right 90 go. (If necessary, explain that when they were first learning how to use the robot, their teacher may have preset the robot to move in 90° turns only and therefore they may have written 'right 1' instead of 'right 90'. Tell the children that they will be using degrees of turn from now on.) Remind them about using 'repeat' by programming the following: repeat 4 [forward 4 right 90]. Discuss with the children their previous experiences of programming the robot. Tell them that there is a computer version of the floor robot called a screen turtle and that they will be learning how to program this.

Group activities

Focus group – with the teacher

- ✦ Introduce the children to the screen turtle. Explain that it works in a very similar way to the floor robot but there are a few differences. One of these is that single instructions typed in will be obeyed immediately, unlike the floor robot which will not obey instructions until the 'go' button is pressed. Demonstrate this by typing in some instructions to show the turtle moving.
- ✦ Point out that the step size used by the screen turtle is much smaller than the floor robot, hence the numbers typed in need to be much larger. Demonstrate this by making the turtle move in a square but use 'forward 100' instead of 'forward 4'. Discuss the spacing between the command and the number, the use of the return (enter) key and the 'clear screen' and 'home' commands.
- ✦ Explain that the commands are still 'forward' and 'back', not 'up' and 'down' the screen and that it is important to spell correctly the commands as the computer will not recognise spelling errors.
- ✦ Then explain that they will be working in pairs or small groups to complete some work using an activity sheet.

Using the photocopiable activity sheets

- ✦ The sheets are to be used at the computer, after the teacher focus session. Remind the children to use 'clear screen' before beginning each new set of instructions.

Plenary session

Share the responses to the activity sheets. Were their predictions correct? Did they have any problems orientating the turtle on screen? What other problems did they have? How did they solve them? What did they learn about using a screen turtle?

Name ______________________ **Activity 1** **Date** ______________________

✦ Using screen turtle – 1 ✦

✦ Type these commands and draw the shape that results.

a) forward 100
right 90
forward 100

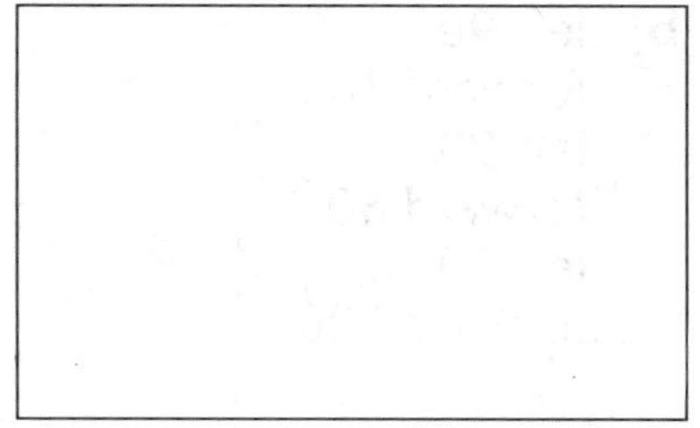

b) forward 100
left 90
forward 100

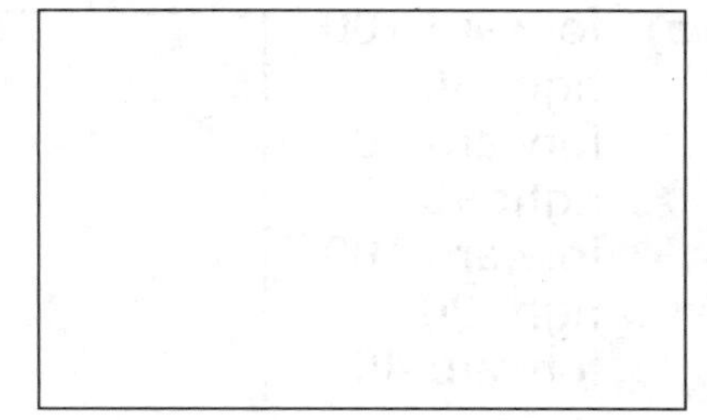

c) forward 100
left 90
forward 100
left 90
forward 100

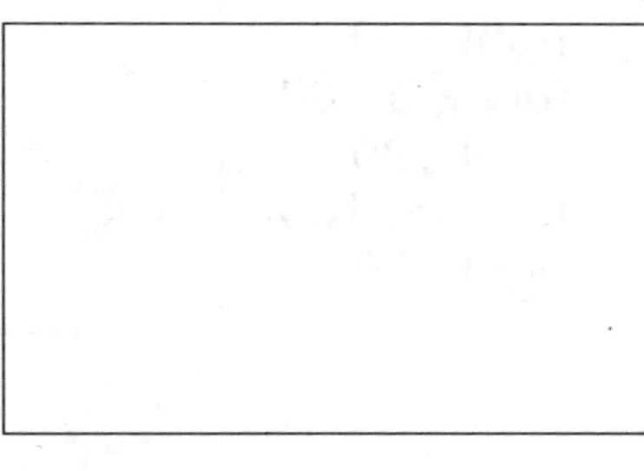

d) forward 100
left 90
forward 50
back 100

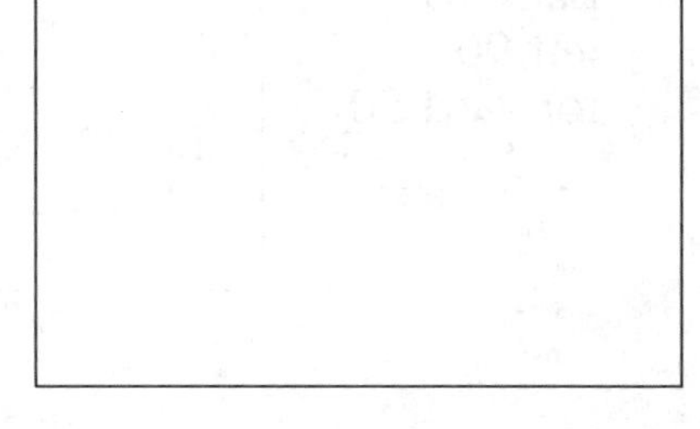

✦ Predict what these commands will draw. Then type in the commands to see if you are correct.

✔ if you are correct

a) left 90
forward 100
right 90
forward 100

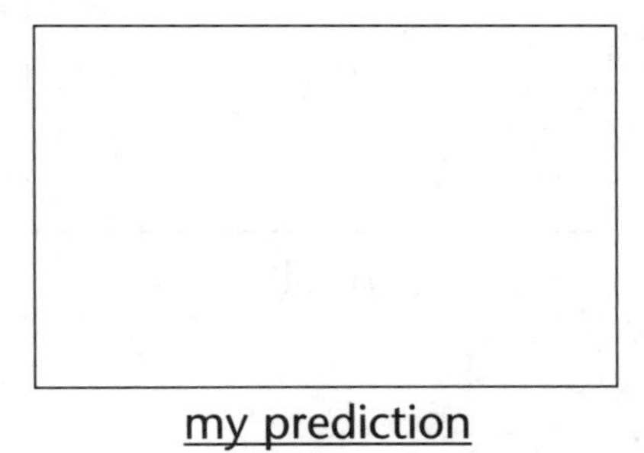

my prediction — result

b) forward 100
right 90
forward 20
right 90
forward 100
right 90
forward 20

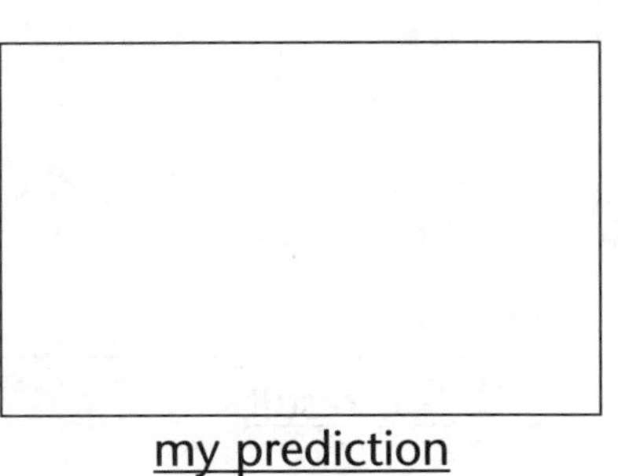

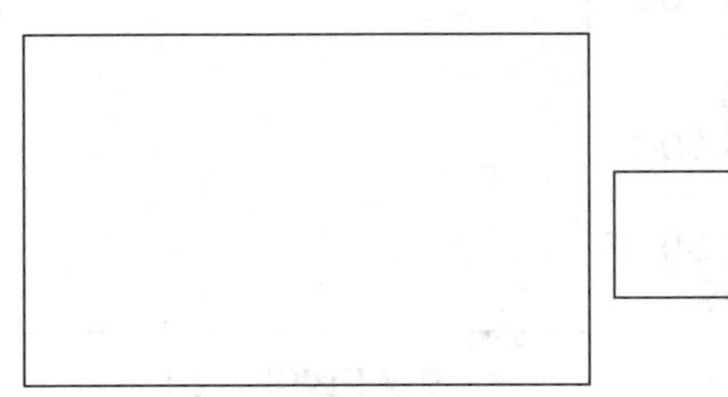

my prediction — result

Name ______________ **Activity 2** **Date** ______________

✦ Using screen turtle – 1 ✦

✦ Type these commands and draw the shape that results.

a) forward 100
right 90
forward 40
right 90
forward 100
right 90
forward 40

b) left 90
forward 100
left 90
forward 50
left 90
forward 100

c) forward 50
back 25
left 90
forward 50

d) forward 100
right 120
forward 100
right 120
forward 100
right 120

✦ Predict what these commands will draw. Then type in the commands to see if you are correct.

✔ if you are correct

a) forward 100
left 90
forward 50
back 100

my prediction | result

b) forward 100
back 50
right 90
forward 50
left 90
forward 50
back 100

my prediction | result

Name ______________________ **Activity 3** **Date** ______________________

✦ Using screen turtle – 1 ✦

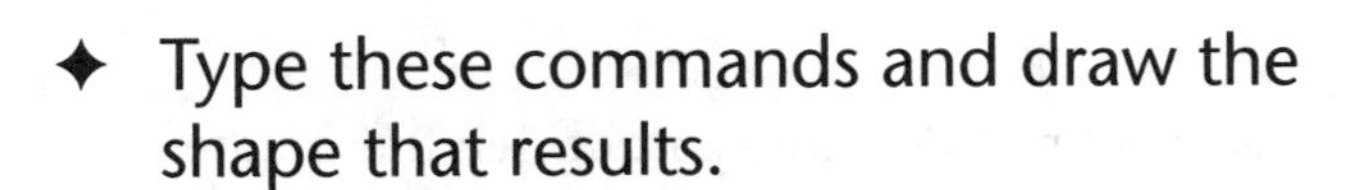

✦ Type these commands and draw the shape that results.

a) forward 50
right 90
forward 50
left 90
forward 50
right 90
forward 50
left 90
forward 50
right 90
forward 50

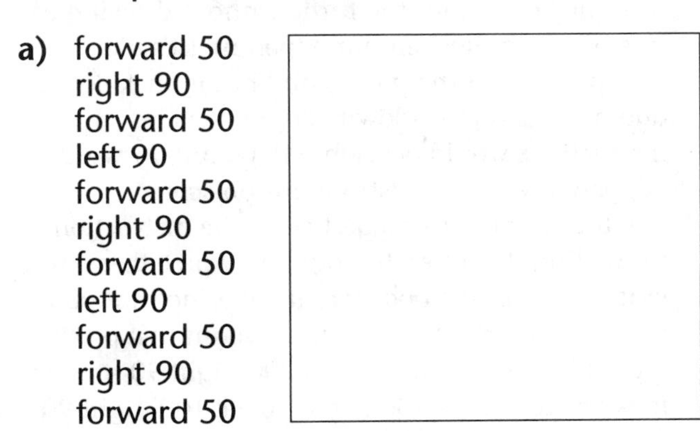

b) right 45
forward 50
right 90
forward 50
left 45
forward 20
left 45
forward 50
right 90
forward 50

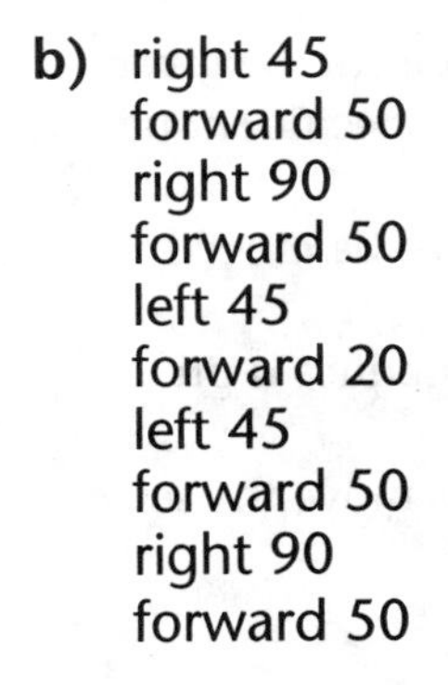

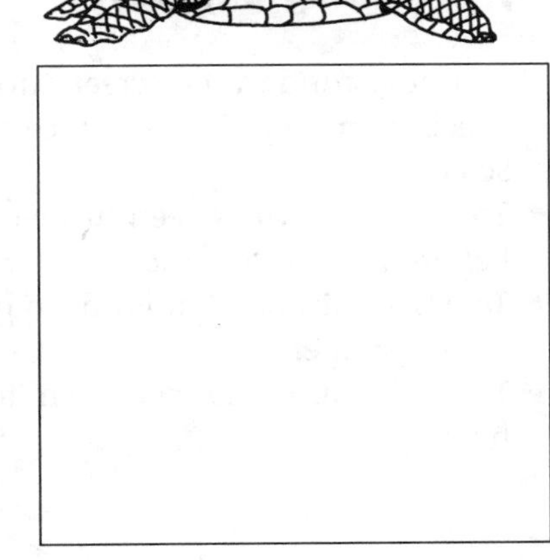

c) forward 100
right 45
forward 50
right 90
forward 50
right 45
forward 100
right 90
forward 70

d) forward 50
right 120
forward 50
right 120
forward 50
right 120

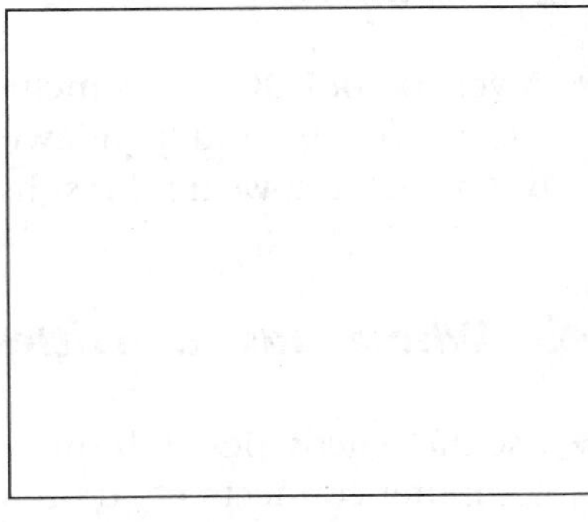

✦ Predict what these commands will draw. Then type in the commands to see if you are correct.

✔ if you are correct

a) forward 100
right 90
forward 50
right 90
forward 50
right 90
forward 50
left 135
forward 70

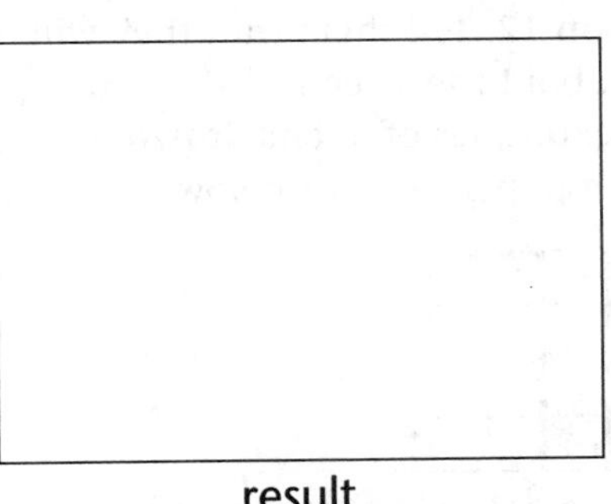

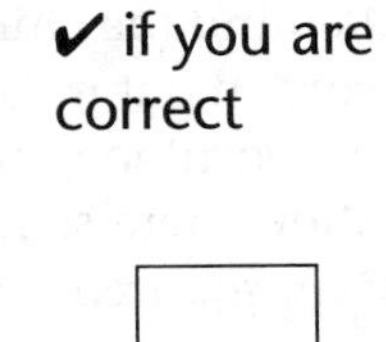

my prediction result

b) left 45
forward 50
left 90
forward 50
right 45
forward 50
right 45
forward 50
left 90
forward 50
home

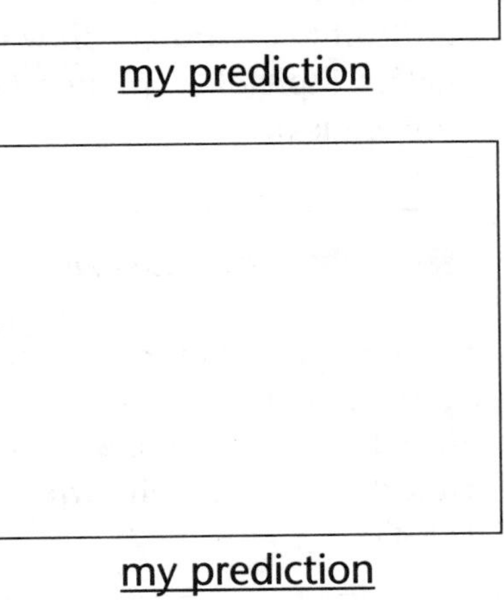

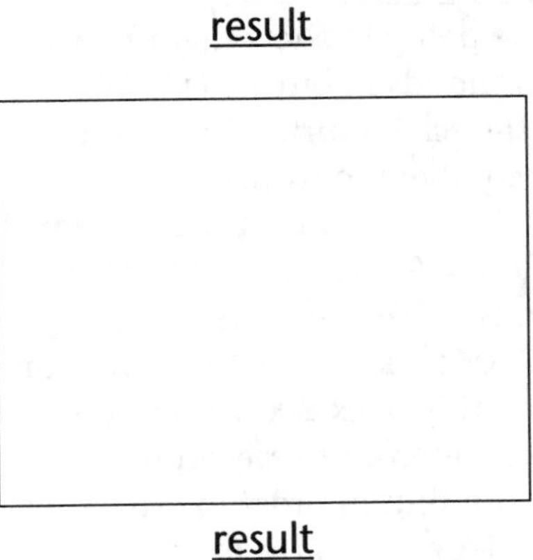

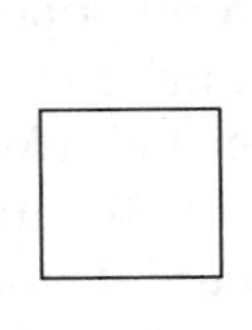

my prediction result

Lesson 13

Using LOGO – writing commands

Learning objectives

- To understand that a screen turtle can be given specific commands to produce a specific shape on screen.
- To know that the screen turtle can be moved before it starts drawing.
- To write a list of commands to produce a pre-drawn shape.
- To use 'penup' and 'pendown' to move the screen turtle.

Resources

- A version of LOGO that includes the commands 'clear', 'penup' and 'pendown' (or equivalent) and which allows final results to be printed out.

Whole class activities

- Use these activities with the whole class using a computer connected to a projected screen or several computers in a suite (or in small groups with one computer over several sessions).
- Remind the children about the activities they carried out in Lesson 12. Tell them that they will be learning more about the screen turtle today.
- Show them some examples of letters drawn on 1cm squared graph paper, such as below.

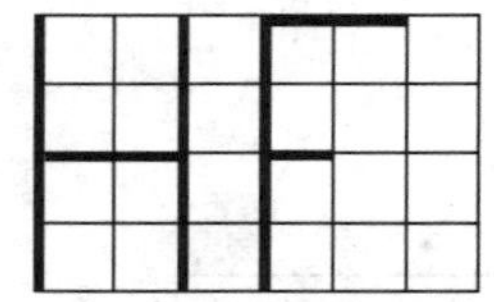

- Explain that you are going to show them how to write their own commands in order to produce these letters using the screen turtle. Say that using graph paper can help them to work out the number of steps and degrees of turn the turtle will need to take (1 square = 50 screen turtle steps).
- Write the instructions for the letter 'H' on the board (ie forward 200 back 100 right 90 forward 100 left 90 forward 100 back 200). Then type them into the LOGO program to see what happens. Now explain that in order to draw the letter 'F' next to this letter, we have to move the screen turtle over to the right. Tell the children that they can move the turtle without drawing a line by using the command 'penup' (it's like lifting a pen off the paper) and put it back down again by using 'pendown'. So the next instructions would be: right 90, penup, forward 50, pendown. Demonstrate this on screen.
- Ask the children to suggest what the instructions for writing the letter 'F' would be. Agree these and write them on the board, remembering that you will need to orientate the turtle again first by typing left 90 (then: forward 200 right 90 forward 100 back 100 left 90 back 100 right 90 forward 50).
- Tell the children that they are now going to use an activity sheet to write the instructions to make a simple word.

Group activities

Using the photocopiable activity sheets

- The sheets are to be used at the computer after the whole class introduction. Ask the children to print out the results.

Note: the instructions on these sheets represent just <u>one</u> way of drawing the letter shapes. The children may find alternative ways.

Drawing letters such as 'N' or 'M' using graph paper as a reference can pose a particular challenge for the children because the diagonals of a square are longer than its sides. This makes it difficult to accurately draw the diagonals in the letters. More able children may like to try and solve this problem!

Plenary session

Share responses to the activity sheets. What problems did they have writing the instructions? How did they solve these problems? Challenge the children to write their own name or words in LOGO.

Name ______________________ **Activity 1** **Date** ______________________

✦ Using screen turtle – 2 ✦

✦ Use the graph paper below to help you complete the instructions to draw the letters in this word.

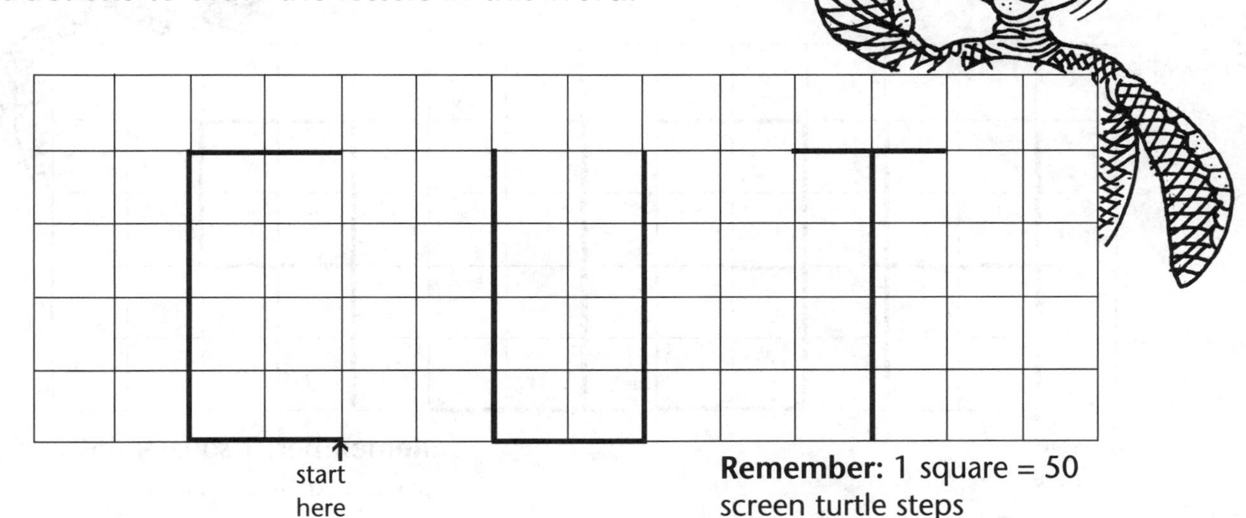

✦ Complete these instructions for the screen turtle.

1 <u>letter 'C'</u>
left 90
forward ________
right 90
forward ________
right ________
forward ________

2 <u>space</u>
penup
forward 100
pendown
right 90

3 <u>letter 'U'</u>
forward 200
________ 90
forward ________
left 90
forward ________
right 90

4 <u>space</u>
penup
forward ________
pendown

5 <u>letter 'T'</u>
forward 100
back 50
right ________
forward ________

✦ Now type these commands into your program to see if you are correct.

Name ____________________ **Activity 2** **Date** ____________________

✦ Using screen turtle – 2 ✦

✦ Use the graph paper below to help you complete the instructions to draw the letters in this word.

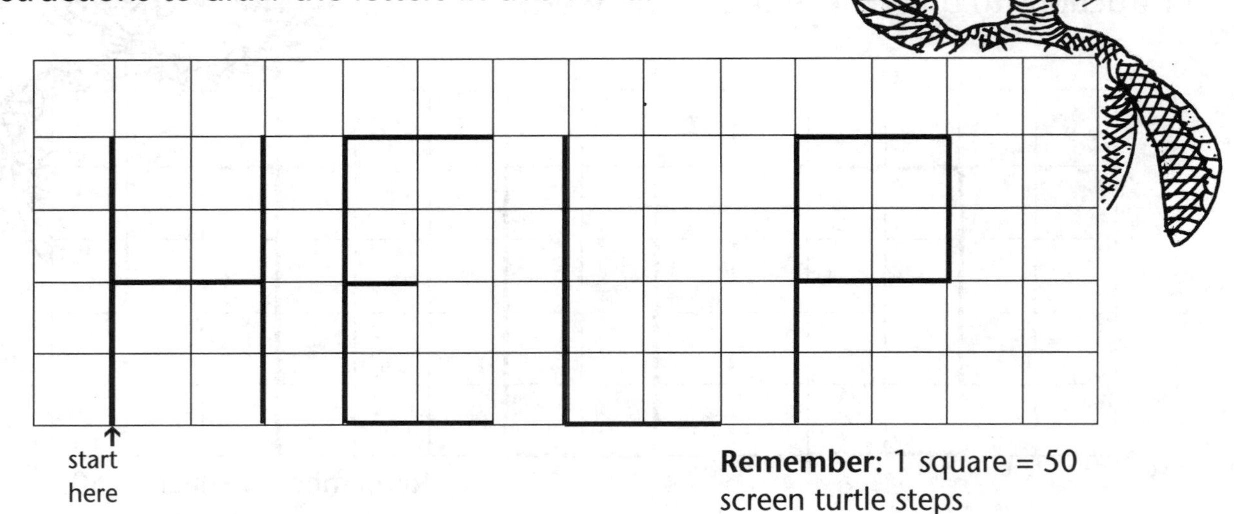

Remember: 1 square = 50 screen turtle steps

✦ Complete these instructions for the screen turtle:

1 letter 'H'
forward 200
back 100
right 90
forward ________
left ________
forward ________
back 200
right 90

2 space
penup
forward 50
pendown

3 letter 'E'
forward 100
back 100
left 90
forward 100
right ________
forward 50
back ________
left ________
foward ________
________ 90
forward 100

4 space
penup
forward ________
pendown
left 90

5 letter 'L'
back ________
right ________
forward ________

6 space
penup
forward ________
pendown
____

7 letter 'P'
forward 200
right ________
forward ________
right 90
forward ________
________ 90
forward 100

✦ Now type these commands into your program to see if you are correct.

Name ____________________ **Activity 3** **Date** ____________________

✦ Using screen turtle – 2 ✦

✦ Use the graph paper below to help you complete the instructions to draw the letters in this word.

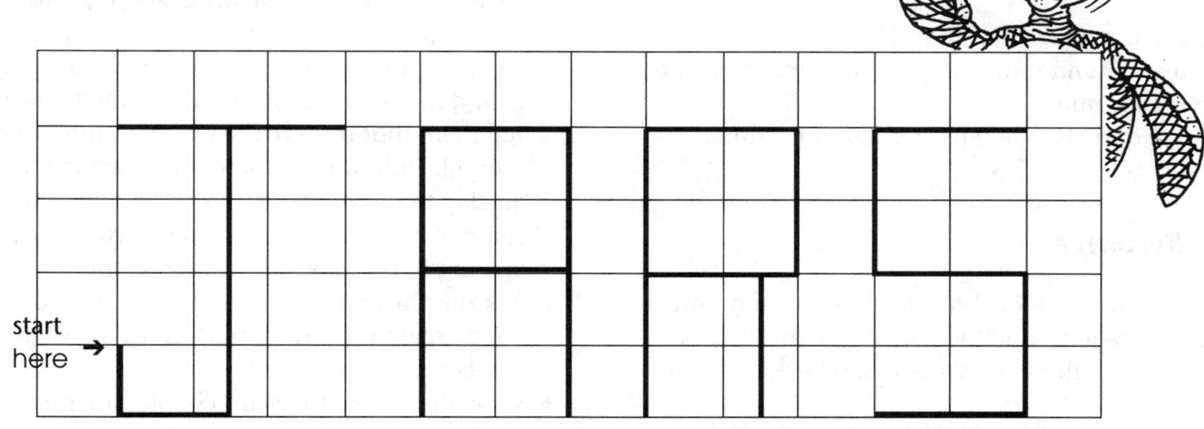

Remember: 1 square = 50 screen turtle steps

✦ Complete these instructions for the screen turtle.

1 letter 'J'
back 50
right 90
forward ______
left 90
forward ______
left _____
forward 75
back _______

2 space
penup
back 50
pendown
left 90

3 letter 'A'
forward 200
back _______
left ______
forward 100
________ 90
forward 100
left 90
forward _______
back ________
_________ 90
forward ________
left 90

4 space
penup
____
pendown

5 letter 'R'
left 90
forward 200
right _______
forward _______
________ 90
forward 100
right 90
forward _______
back _______
________ 90
forward 100
left 90

6 space
penup
forward ______
pendown

7 letter 'S'
forward 100
left ______
forward _______
________ 90
forward _______
right _______
__________ 100
right 90
____

✦ Now type these commands into your program to see if you are correct.

Lesson 14

Using LOGO – procedures

Learning objectives

- To use the repeat command.
- To understand that groups of instructions can be given a name.
- To use and change a pre-written procedure.

Resources

- A version of LOGO that includes the commands 'clear', 'penup' and 'pendown' (or equivalent) and which allows final results to be printed out.

Whole class activities

- Use these activities with the whole class using a computer connected to a projected screen (or computer suite) or within small groups over several sessions. Before the lesson write the following procedures into the computer and save them.

```
to square
repeat 4 [forward 50 right 90]
end

to triangle
repeat 3 [forward 50 right 120]
end

to octagon
repeat 8 [forward 50 right 45]
end
```

- Remind the children how they used the repeat command with the floor turtle. Tell them that they can also use this command with the screen turtle.
- Type the following into the LOGO program: repeat 4 [forward 50 right 90] and ask the children to watch what happens. Show them which brackets to use on the keyboard and where the spacing should go. Then ask them to type in the sequence themselves.
- Write up the following instruction: repeat 3 [forward 50 right 120] and ask the children to predict how many sides they think the shape will have. Type in the sequence to see if they are right.
- Explain that if they wanted to draw two triangles next to each other, they would have to type the procedure once, use 'penup' and 'pendown' commands and then type the triangle procedure once more. Demonstrate this. Say that this can be a bit of a chore, so it is possible to 'teach' the computer to 'remember' how to draw a triangle by typing in the instructions and giving it a name. Tell them that this is called a 'procedure'. Type 'triangle' into the computer to show them how quickly the computer draws it. Tell them that the computer only knows this word because you have previously typed in the procedure and saved it.
- Ask the children to try the other procedures you have previously saved, that is: square and octagon.
- Show them how they can change the procedures to alter the size of the shapes by altering the numbers.
- Tell them that they will now be using an activity sheet to predict and test out repeat instructions and to change procedures.

Group activities

Using the photocopiable activity sheets

- The sheets are to be used at the computer after the whole class introduction. Ask the children to print out their results.

Plenary session

Share the responses to the activity sheets. Were their predictions correct? Were they able to successfully change the procedures to alter the size of the shapes? What did they notice when they were doing this? What problems did they have? Ask someone using Activity sheet 3 to explain their final task. Share the different results. Challenge the children to write their own procedures.

Name ____________________ **Activity 1** Date ____________________

✦ Using screen turtle – 3 ✦

✦ Predict how many sides these instructions will draw. Then type them in to see if you are correct.

	Instructions	Number of sides I think it will draw	Name of shape	Put a ✔ if you are right
1	repeat 4 [forward 150 right 90]			
2	repeat 3 [forward 150 right 120]			
3	repeat 5 [forward 100 right 72]			

✦ Now work out how to make all of these shapes smaller! Try it out on the computer and write down the instruction you used for each shape here. The first one has been done for you.

1 repeat 4 [forward 50 right 90]

2

3

✦ Type in the square and octagon procedures. Work out how to change them to make the shapes larger. Write down what you did here.

Name ____________________ **Activity 2** **Date** ____________________

✦ Using screen turtle – 3 ✦

✦ Predict how many sides these instructions will draw. Then type them in to see if you are correct.

	Instructions	Number of sides I think it will draw	Name of shape	Put a ✔ if you are right
1	repeat 6 [forward 150 right 60]			
2	repeat 7 [forward 50 right 51.5]			
3	repeat 9 [forward 50 right 40]			

✦ Now work out how to make all of these shapes smaller! Try it out on the computer and write down the instruction you used for each shape here.

1

2

3

✦ Type in the triangle and octagon procedures. Work out how to change them to make the shapes larger. Write down what you did here.

Name ____________________ **Activity 3** Date ____________________

✦ Using screen turtle – 3 ✦

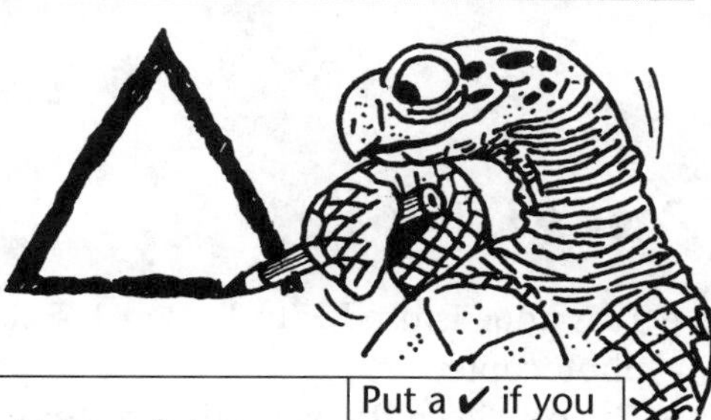

✦ Predict how many sides these instructions will draw.
Then type them in to see if you are correct.

	Instructions	Number of sides I think it will draw	Name of shape	Put a ✔ if you are right
1	repeat 10 [forward 40 right 36]			
2	repeat 11 [forward 50 right 32.8]			
3	repeat 12 [forward 50 right 30]			

✦ Now work out how to make all of these shapes smaller and larger!
Try it out on the computer and write down the instructions you used for each shape here.

smaller	larger
1	1
2	2
3	3
✦ Type in this procedure: repeat 25 [triangle right 20]. Print out what happens, cut it out and glue the design on the back of this sheet.	✦ Now change the procedure to alter the design. Print out your result, cut it out and glue it on the back of this sheet.

✦ Appendix ✦

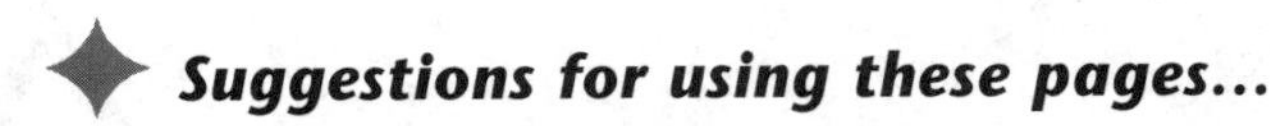

Suggestions for using these pages...

Page 63

- This page is used with Lesson 1. Enlarge it on a photocopier.
- The article could be used as a stimulus for the children to write their own newspaper reports using a word-processor. Perhaps they could write a follow-up report – did Mrs Hunniford's actions have any effect on Mr Marshall's behaviour?

Page 64

- This page is used with Lesson 2. Enlarge it on a photocopier.
- The children could use the instructions to grow their own potatoes. They could use a word-processor to write up a report on what happens.

Page 65

- This page is used with Lesson 3. Enlarge it on a photocopier.
- The children could also use the page as a starting point to find out more information about the greenhouse effect by using a CD-Rom encyclopaedia.

Page 66

- This page is used with Lesson 4. Enlarge it on a photocopier.
- The children could word-process a book about Alex – telling others how to be kind to the environment. The book could be added to the class or school library.

Pages 67 and 68

- These pages are used with Lesson 5.

Page 69

- This page is used with Lesson 6.

Page 70

- This page is used with Lesson 7. Photocopy the page and cut out the pictures.
- The pictures could also be put into a book and the children could use a CD-Rom encyclopaedia to find out information about each creature. The information could then be word processed for the book.

Page 71

- This page is used with Lesson 7. Enlarge it on a photocopier to make a bigger version.

Page 72

- This page is used with Lesson 7. Photocopy and enlarge the face outline so each child has a copy. The instructions are for the teacher on how to play the game.

Page 73

- This page is used with Lesson 8. This information explains how a branching database works and is for teacher use only.

Page 74

- This page is used with Lesson 10.
- The children could also compare these graphs with their own class results.

Page 75

- This page is used with Lesson 11.
- The children could also compare these graphs with the temperatures of a local city.

Page 76

- This is an individual record sheet for recording the skills and knowledge achieved in ICT.

✦ Newspaper headlines ✦

Mr Graham Marshall was left stunned yesterday afternoon when he was attacked by an elderly lady brandishing a large golfing umbrella!

Other residents in Stoke Street were equally shocked when they heard that the usually meek and mild Mrs Gwen Hunniford had attacked Mr Marshall as he left his home on Friday morning.

Mr Marshall had no idea why Mrs Hunniford suddenly decided to hit out at him with her umbrella but he told reporters that she kept on repeating that he was a 'wasteful, uncaring person who should know better'!

Mrs Hunniford later told reporters that she was angry with Mr Marshall because he was constantly throwing away cans, bottles and newspapers instead of recycling them. Mrs Hunniford has been a member of the Stratton Environmental Action Group for the last 25 years and she is concerned that people still don't seem to have got the message about recycling.

Mrs Hunniford said she had spoken to Mr Marshall on many occasions in the past about his wasteful behaviour but he ignored her. So when she saw his rubbish bins overflowing once again, she lost all self-control and finally lashed out!

Frail Lady Attacks Man in Street!

ANGER OVER WASTE PROBLEM

Local Resident Under Attack

TROUBLE OVER RECYCLING

MAN ATTACKED IN STREET

Are Residents Safe in Stoke Street?

✦ Growing potatoes ✦

What you need:	What to do:	Things to know:

Keep the soil damp by watering as necessary.

When the whole plant dies, tip the bucket up and collect the potatoes.

compost

It is best to plant the potato in early spring or autumn.

soil

hammer and large nail

Rub off all but 2 of the strongest shoots from the sprouting potato.

Make some drainage holes in the bottom of the bucket using the hammer and nail.

gardening fork

large bucket

Green shoots should appear 3-4 weeks after planting.

a sprouting potato

water

Stop watering the plant when the flowers have died.

Make a hole in the soil large enough for the potato.

Watering the plant after the flowers have died may cause the potatoes to rot.

As shoots appear, keep covering them with soil until the bucket is full of soil.

Half fill the bucket with soil and mix in a little compost.

Put the potato in the hole and cover it with soil.

✦ The Greenhouse effect ✦

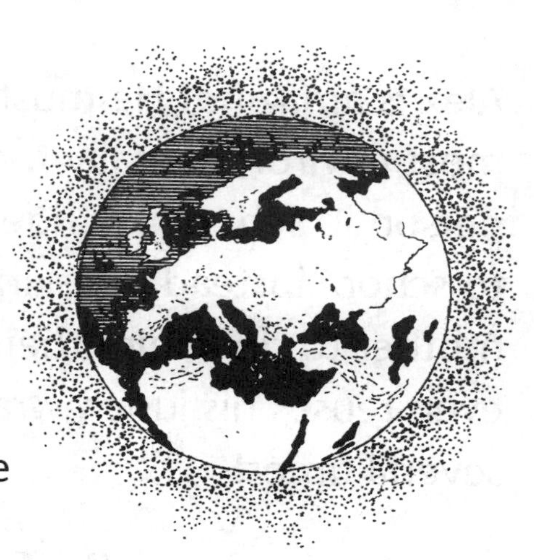

High in the Earth's atmosphere, 'greenhouse' gases allow the son's heet to pass threw to the Earth. The heet warms the land and sea and is than reflected back. The greenhouse gases act like a blancket and trap the heet, stopping it from escapeing into space (like glass traps heet in a greenhouse). Greenhouse gases include: carbon dioxide, nitrous oxide, methane and chloroflurocarbons or CFCs.

If the greenhouse effect did not happen, the Earth would be a frozen plaice with nothing living here. But the problem at the momant is that there are too many greenhouse gases being produced and this is causeing the Earth to warm up too much. This 'global warming' could cause droughts in lots of countrys. The ice caps at the North and South Poles may melt, causeing sea levals to rise. This meens that there would be even less land for things to live and grow and it would be a disaster for peeple living in low-lying countrys such as Bangladesh and islands in the Pacific.

What is causeing more grenhouse gases to be produced? Industrys and power stations that burn fossil fuels and countrys that burn rainforests are releesing lots of carbon dioxide. Cars also prodcue carbon dioxide and nitrogen oxide in their exhoust fewmes. Methane gas is produced from landfill rubbish dumps, rice paddy feilds and cattle. Aorosols, plastic products and fridges can all contains CFCs.

✦ All about Alex ✦

Alex is amazing! He must be the most environmentally-friendly person in school! He rides his bike to school instead of asking his mother to drive him there and he even reuses his lunch wrapping several times!

Alex recycles just about everything! He sorts all the family rubbish into different bins that he helps his mum take to the recycling centre. He has bins for newspapers and magazines, glass, cans and old clothes. He puts all the fruit and vegetable scraps on the family compost heap and he has found a shop that will reuse his egg boxes. He reuses plastic containers to put things in or grow plants in and his dog eats the food scraps.

When Alex goes to the supermarket with his dad he always tries to buy organic food. He takes his own carrier bags and always buys products with little packaging or packaging that can be recycled.

✦ Repeating patterns – 1 ✦

Egyptian patterns

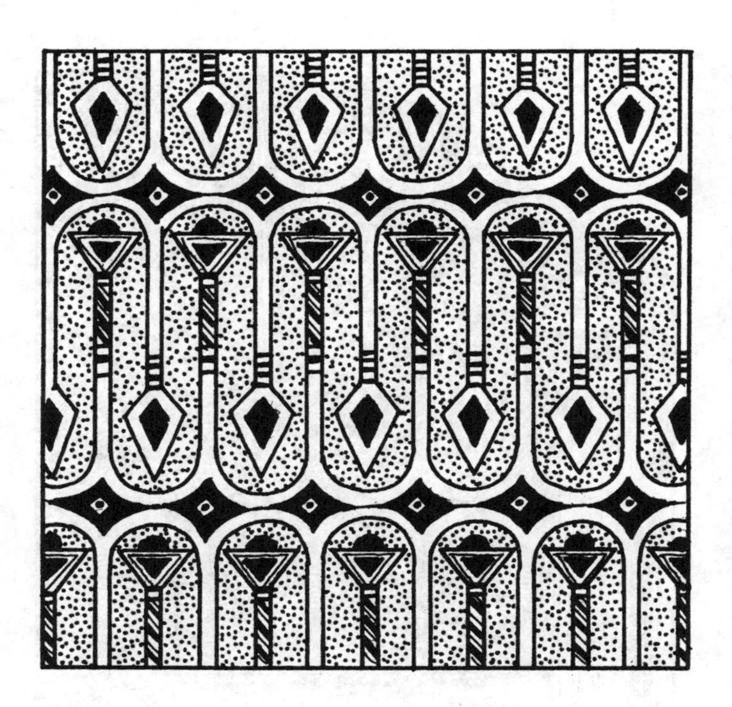

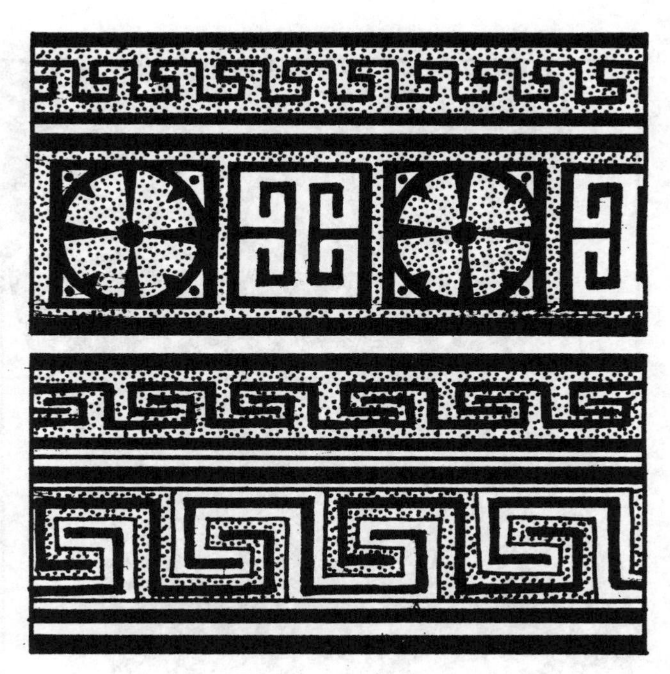

Celtic patterns

✦ Repeating patterns – 2 ✦

Modern repeating patterns such as found on clothing, furniture and wallpaper.

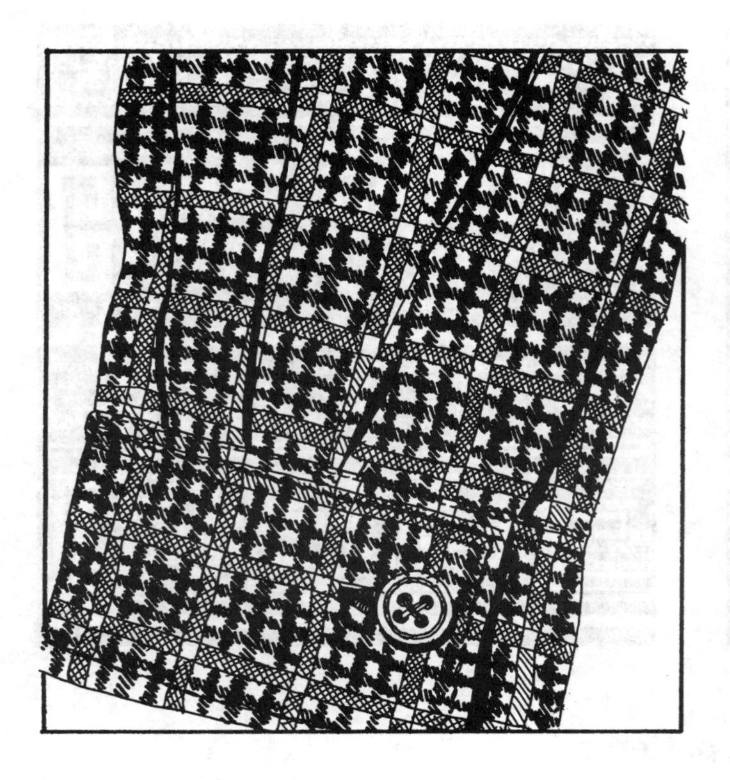

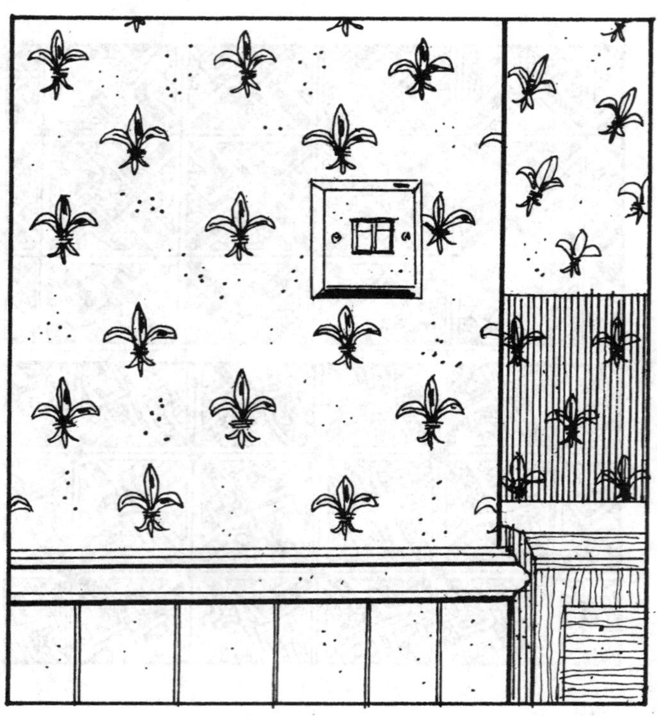

Photocopiable

✦ Symmetrical patterns ✦

Egyptian patterns

Celtic patterns

✦ Animals ✦

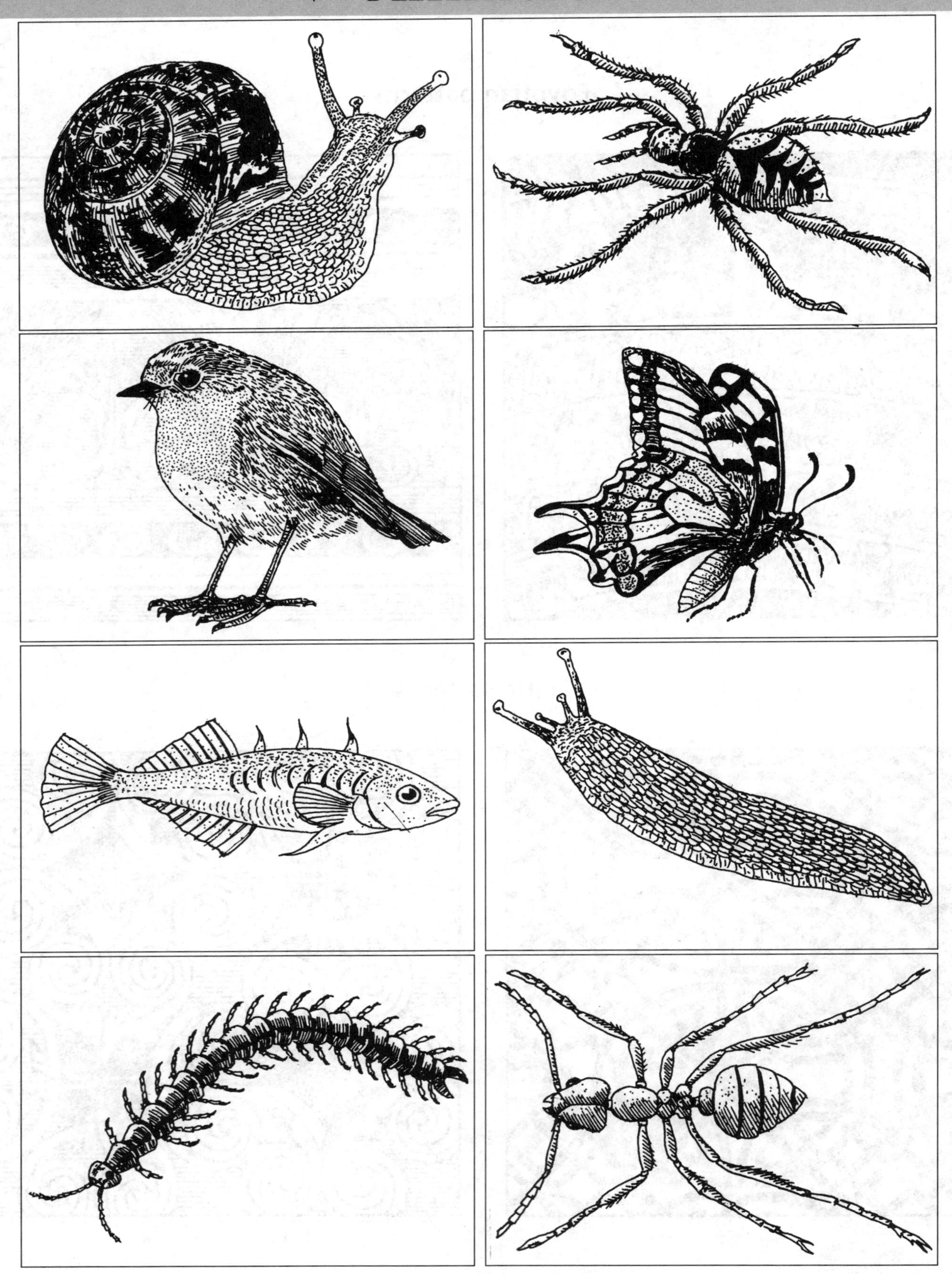

Photocopiable

✦ Tree diagram ✦

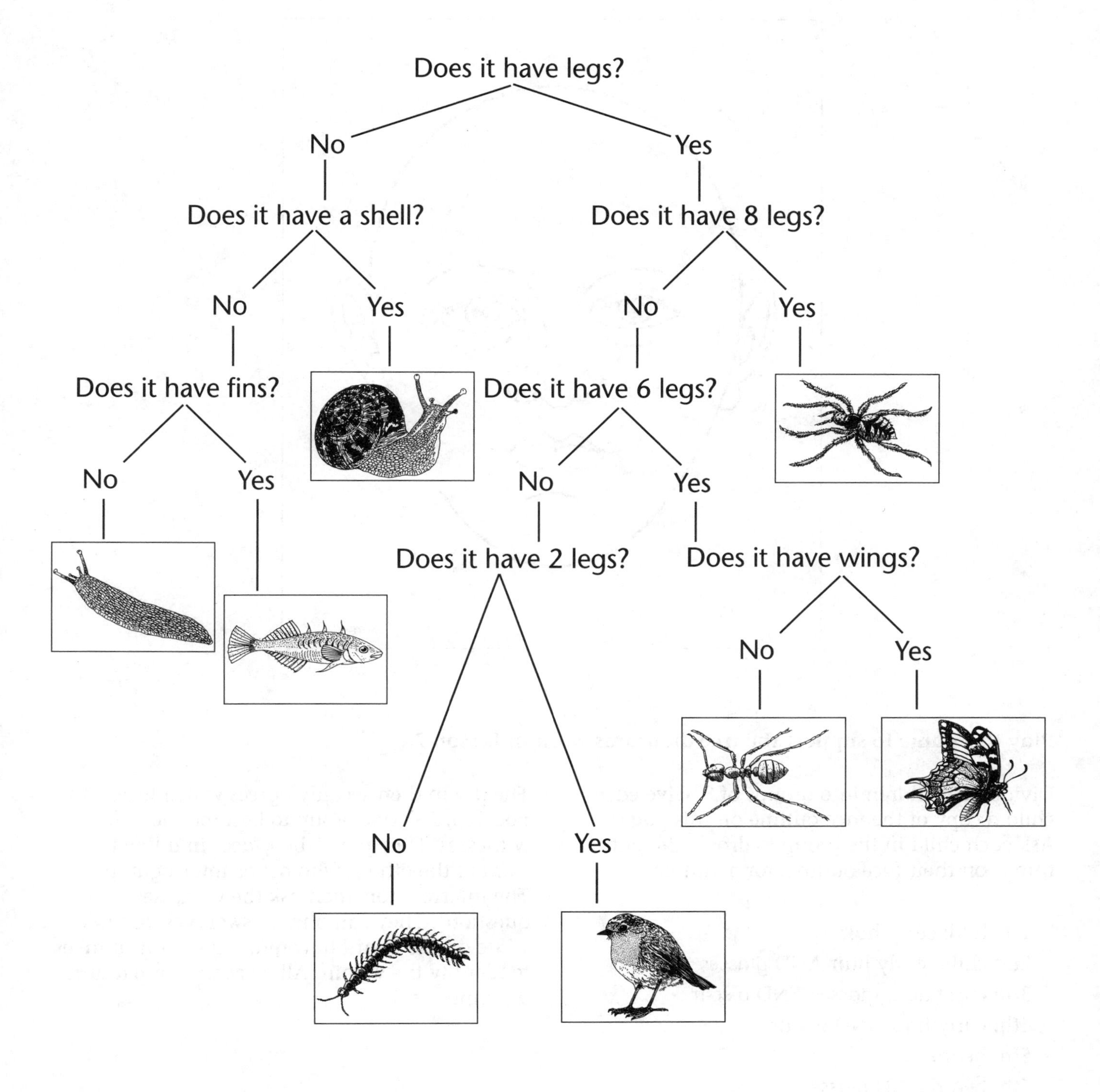

✦ Face game ✦

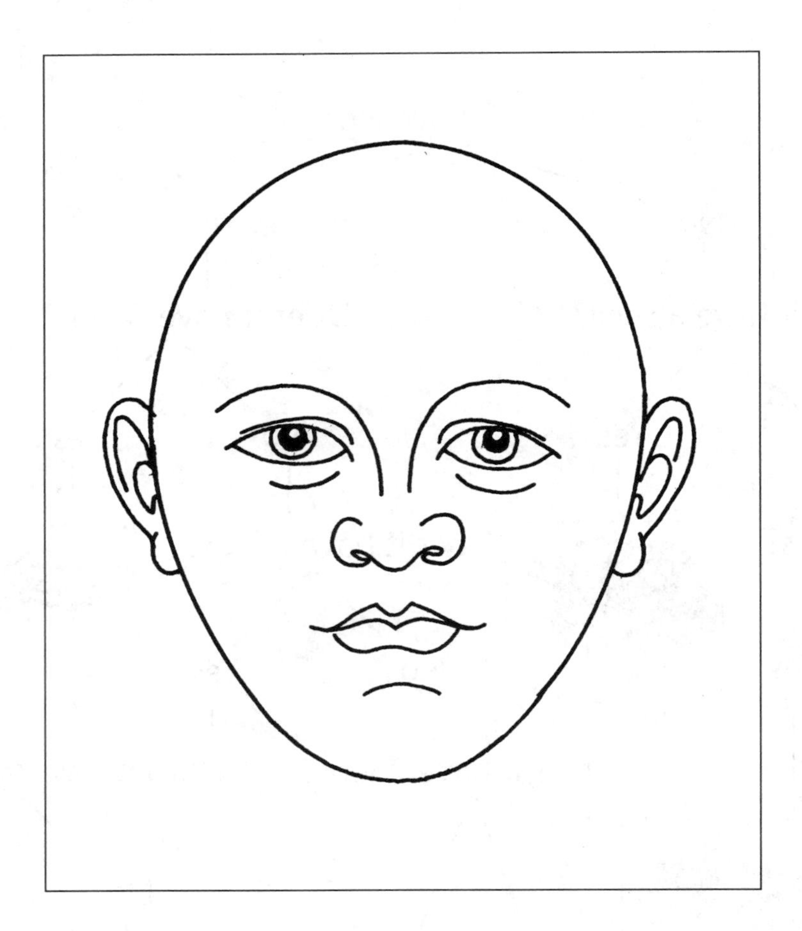

Play this game to support the tree diagrams work in Lesson 7.

Divide the children into groups of 8. Give each child a copy of the face outline on this page. Ask each child in the group to draw different things on their face outline, for example:

1st child: curly hair
2nd child: curly hair AND glasses
3rd: curly hair, glasses AND a scar
4th: curly hair AND a scar
5th: beard
6th: beard AND glasses
7th: beard, glasses AND a scar
8th: beard AND a scar

The group then secretly agrees which face is the poacher. Ask one group to become the witnesses. They place their faces in a line in front of the others, who act as interrogators. The interrogators then ask the witnesses questions. They can only answer 'yes' or 'no'. Write on the board how many questions it takes to identify the villain. Allow each group a turn as witnesses.

✦ Branching databases ✦

This activity explains how branching databases work and is to be used with Lesson 8. It can be carried out with a small group at one computer or with the whole class and a projected screen.

Explain to the children that computers know nothing until people put information into them and that we call this 'programming'. Explain that they are going to program the computer to play a game with them. The game is called 'Can you guess what form of transport I am thinking about?' (Note: you must use a branching database, not an ordinary one.)

The database will ask you to name your file. Call it 'Transport'. It might then ask you what the game is about. It might also ask you 'If two things are called "methods of transport", what is one called?' (The questions may seem clumsy, but try to answer them as best as you can.) For example, one would be called 'method of transport' (not 'methods').

The computer will prompt you for a question that separates the examples given. For example, if we entered 'bus' and 'pram', the question could be 'Do you need a ticket to use this form of transport?' The computer might then ask you to answer 'yes' or 'no' for pram. Enter the correct response.

The computer may then offer to play a game. It will ask you to think of a method of transport and it will try to guess what it is. Ask a child to think of a method of transport, for example a bike. The computer will ask the question 'Do you need a ticket to use this form of transport?' The child should select 'no'. The computer may then guess 'Is it a pram?' The child should select 'no'. The computer will then ask for a question that distinguishes a pram from a bike. The child enters a question and the computer will then offer to play a game again.

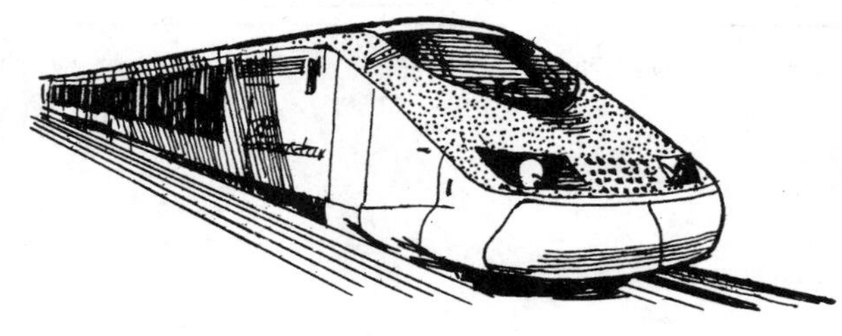

✦ Graphs – 1 ✦

How we travel to school – Class 4

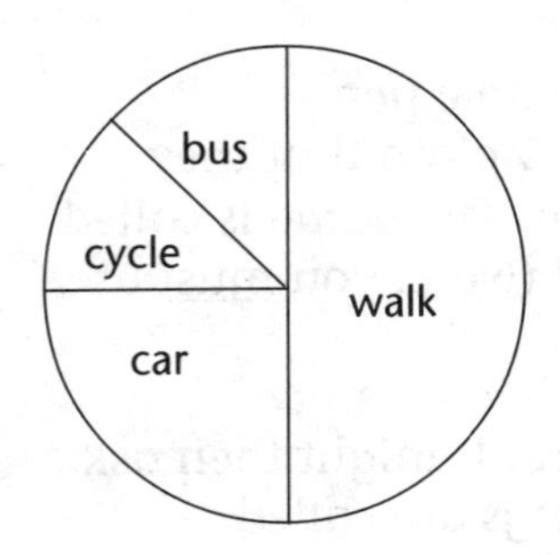

How we travel to school – Preston Primary

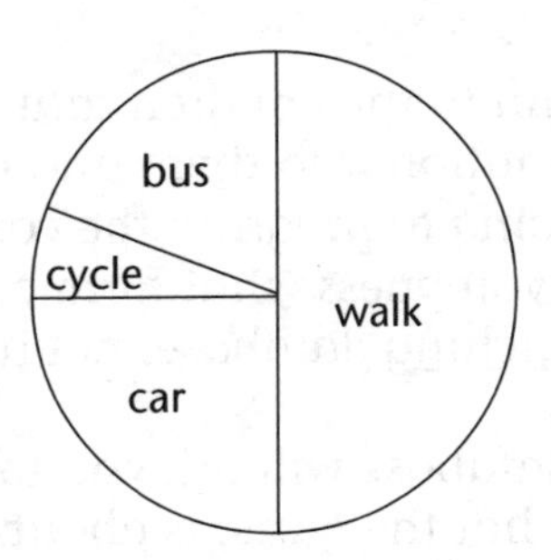

How we travel to school – Class 4

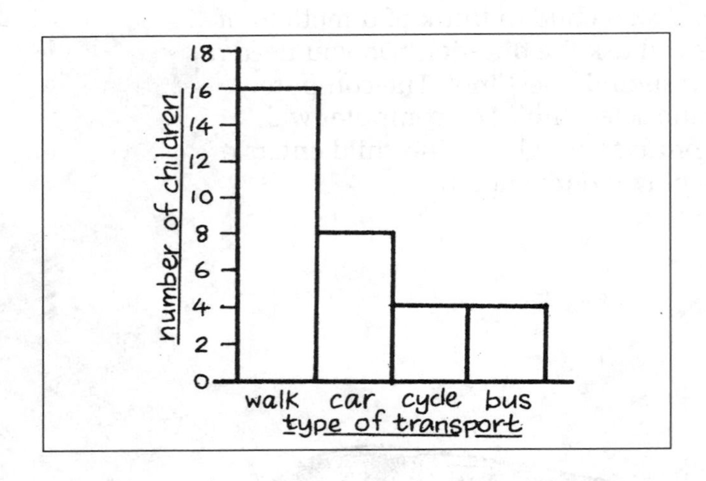

How we travel to school – Preston Primary

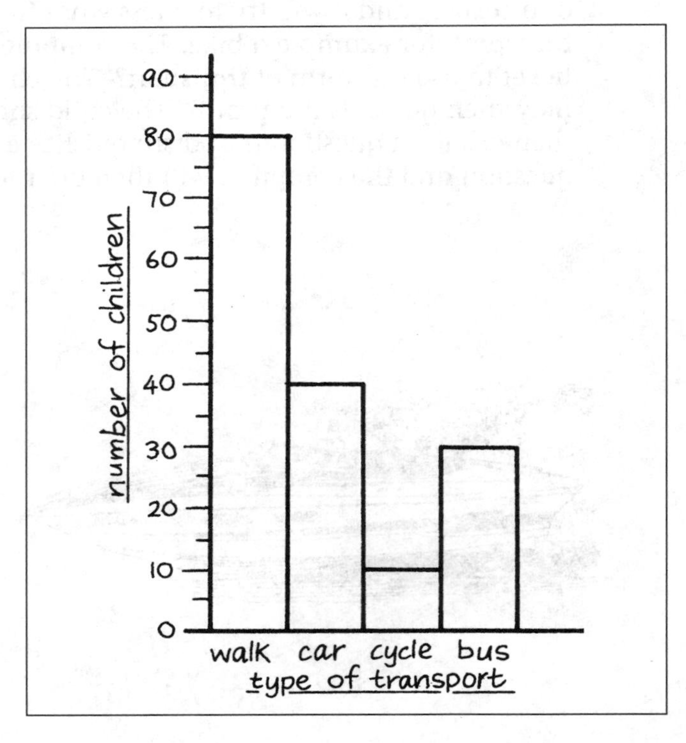

✦ Graphs – 2 ✦

Daily temperatures in Sydney – 13th to 19th March

1. Bar-chart

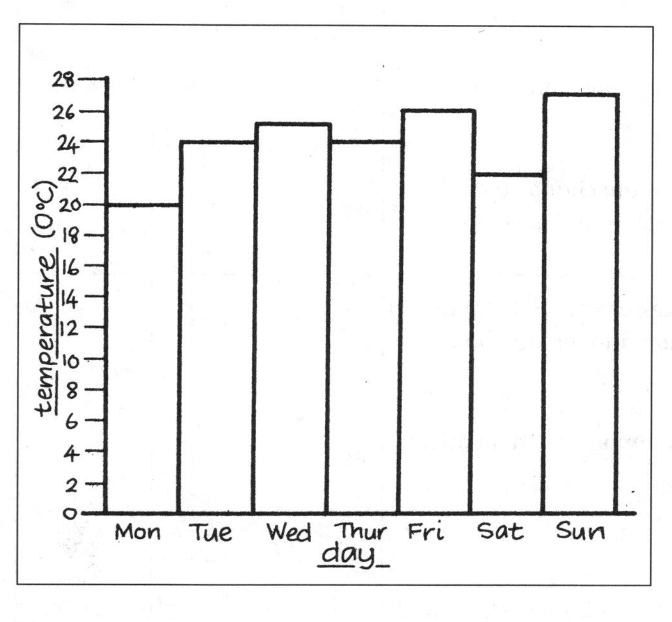

2. Pie chart

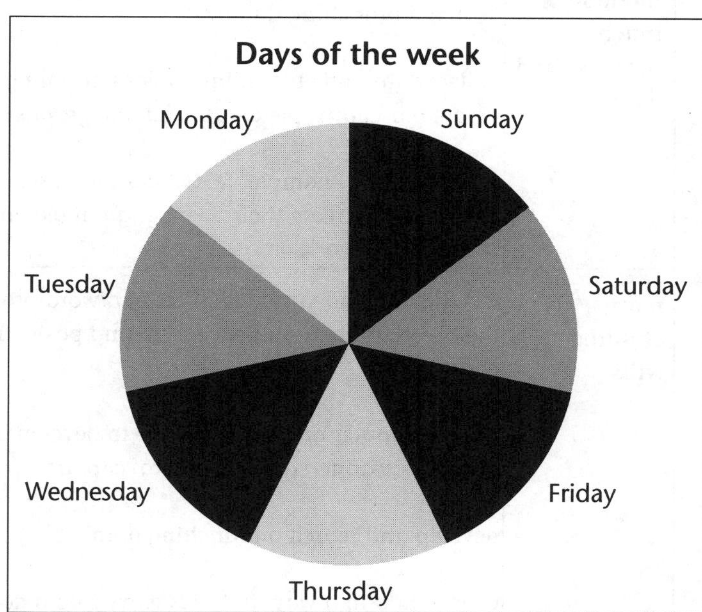

3. Bar line chart

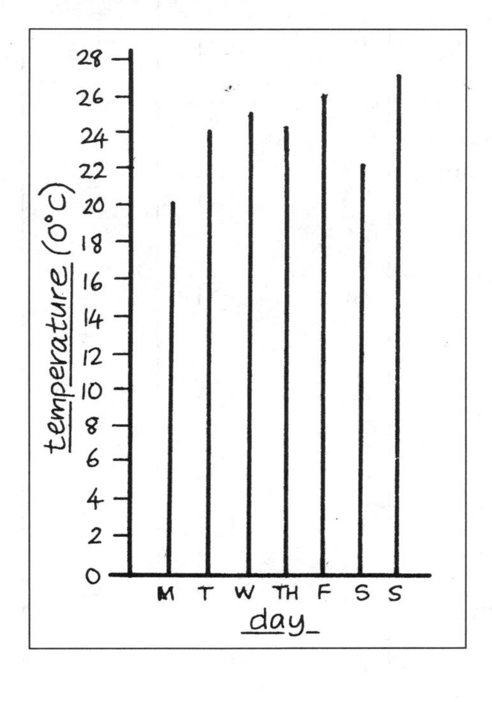

4. Line graph

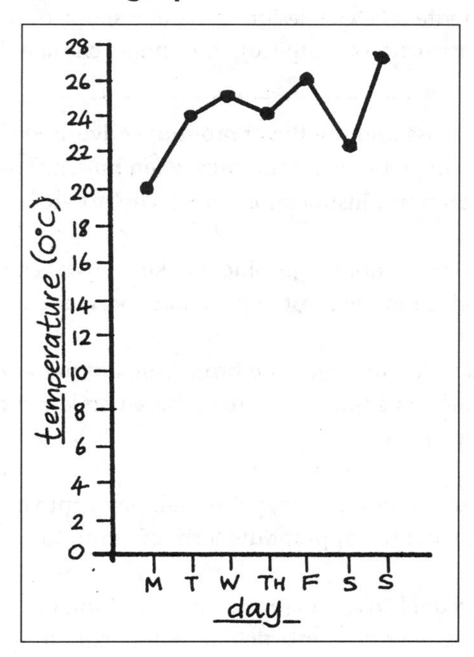

ICT Assessment

Name__________________ Year__________ Date__________ Level__________

Tick the boxes and look for best fit when assessing level.

QCA Expectations		QCA SOW Unit		NC level
some children will not have made so much progress and will:	use features such as spell-check to help them edit their work	4A	☐	2-3
	use a computer graphics package to develop an image	4B	☐	
	search a branching database	4C	☐	
	collect data and enter it into a data handling package and use it to create bar-charts, pie charts and line graphs	4D	☐	
	work from an example LOGO design on screen and change the procedure to create their own design; make mistakes and need to amend their work	4E	☐	
most children will:	use the more advanced features of a word-processor to help them match their work to their audience – cut and paste, find and replace, bold, change font	4A	☐	3-4
	use a computer graphics package to develop an image using a variety of tools – scanner, digital camera, clip art	4B	☐	
	develop and search a branching database	4C	☐	
	collect data in a way that aids entry into a data handling package and use it to create bar-charts, pie charts and line graphs	4D	☐	
	create a LOGO design using one shape and rotating it; use the repeat instruction to duplicate the shape; change the angle of turn	4E	☐	
some children will have progressed further and will:	choose and use the appropriate advanced features of a word-processor to increase their efficiency when matching their audience – thesaurus, tab stops, justification, italic, clip art etc	4A	☐	4
	use a computer graphics package to develop and refine an image selecting the most appropriate tools, and saving drafts	4B	☐	
	develop and search a branching database using efficient criteria – questions that are focused, based on key characteristics which sort quickly	4C	☐	
	collect data in a way that aids entry into a data handling package and choose the appropriate form of graph to represent it	4D	☐	
	create LOGO designs using more than one shape and rotating them; use the repeat instruction to duplicate shapes; investigate more complex shapes and sizes; change the angle of turn	4E	☐	